Rasterelektronenmikroskopie

Scanning Electron Microscopy

Rasterelektronenmikroskopie
Eine Einführung für Mediziner und Biologen

Scanning Electron Microscopy
An Introduction for Physicians and Biologists

J. Ohnsorge and R. Holm
Foreword G. Pfefferkorn
Translated by J. Yeo

Zweite überarbeitete und erweiterte Auflage
Second revised and enlarged edition

143 Figures

Georg Thieme Publishers Stuttgart 1978

Autoren:
Prof. Dr. med. JOCHEN OHNSORGE
Orthopädische Universitätsklinik Köln
Joseph-Stelzmann-Str. 9, 5000 Köln 41 (Germany)

Diplom-Physiker Dr. REIMER HOLM
Ingenieurbereich Angewandte Physik, Bayer AG
5090 Leverkusen (Germany)

Übersetzer:
JULIAN YEO
Allensteiner Str. 1
5090 Leverkusen 1 (Germany)

CIP-Kurztitelaufnahme der Deutschen Bibliothek

Ohnsorge, Jochen
Rasterelektronenmikroskopie :
e. Einf. für Mediziner u. Biologen /
J. Ohnsorge and R. Holm. –
2., überarb. u. erw. Aufl. –
Stuttgart : Thieme, 1978.
    ISBN 3-13-502302-8
NE: Holm, Reimer:

1. Auflage 1973

Herrn
Prof. Dr. med. G. IMHÄUSER, Köln
zum 65. Geburtstag
gewidmet

Dedicated to
Prof. Dr. med. G. IMHÄUSER, Cologne
on the occasion of his
65th birthday

Geleitwort

Die noch sehr junge Untersuchungsmethode der Rasterelektronenmikroskopie hat erst 1965 ihren Einzug in die anwendenden Wissenschaften gehalten. Seitdem hat sie einen kaum vorherzusehenden Aufschwung auf allen jenen Gebieten erfahren, für die die mikroskopische Erforschung von Oberflächen bedeutsam ist, und zwar nicht zuletzt dank der bildhaft plastischen Darstellungen, die diese Methode ermöglicht. Deshalb eignet sich die Rasterelektronenmikroskopie besonders für Mediziner und Biologen zur räumlichen Darstellung von inneren und äußeren Oberflächen, deren Feinaufbau mit anderen Methoden oft nur unzulänglich oder nur mit größerem Aufwand erfaßt werden kann.

Bei der heutigen Verbreitung der Rasterelektronenmikroskopie ist es selbst für den Fachmann schon nicht mehr leicht, den vollen Überblick über die vielfältigen Einsatzmöglichkeiten in den verschiedensten Wissensbereichen und über die speziellen Präparationsmethoden für eine erfolgreiche Anwendung dieser neuartigen elektronenmikroskopischen Untersuchungstechnik zu behalten. Daher ist es eine verdienstvolle Arbeit der Verfasser, einem breiteren Publikum diesen illustrativen Einführungsband vorzulegen. Er vermittelt auch dem entfernter Stehenden einen klar gegliederten, kurzen Überblick über die Grundlagen und die wesentlichen Verfahrensweisen dieser Methodik. Besonders eindrucksvoll wird hierbei die große Auswahl guter Bildbeispiele auf den Betrachter wirken und ihm die Anwendungsbreite der Rasterelektronenmikroskopie deutlich vor Augen führen.

Ich bin überzeugt, dieses Buch wird manchen Leser an diese neue Untersuchungsmethode heranführen, ihn zu eigenen Arbeiten anregen und damit schließlich zur weiteren Verbreitung der Rasterelektronenmikroskopie beitragen.

Im November 1972

Prof. Dr. G. PFEFFERKORN
Direktor des Institutes für
Medizinische Physik der
Universität Münster

Foreword

The relatively new surface investigation technique of scanning electron microscopy was introduced for the applied sciences as recently as 1965. Since then, unforeseen expansion has occurred in all those fields for which microscopic research on surfaces is important, in part due to the lifelike image presentation which the method employs. It is for this reason that scanning electron microscopy is especially useful to physicians and biologists, permitting three-dimensional imaging of internal and external surfaces whose fine structure cannot adequately be visualised by other techniques.

With today's widespread application of scanning electron microscopy, it is no longer easy, even for a specialist, to keep abreast either of the potential of the technique in different fields or of special preparative techniques for its successful application. Therefore it·must be considered a special merit of the authors to submit this illustrative introductory volume to the general public. The book gives a clearly presented, brief, overall review of the fundamental theory and essential operating techniques of the method, suited also to readers with little previous knowledge of the subject. The large selection of good image illustrations will be particularly impressive to the reader and will show him the breadth of application of scanning electron microscopy.

I am convinced that this book will lead many a reader to this new examination technique, will stimulate him to work with it, and thus eventually contribute to the further distribution of scanning electron microscopy.

November, 1972

Prof. Dr. G. PFEFFERKORN
Director of the Institute
of Medical Physics at the
University of Münster, Germany

Vorwort zur 2. Auflage

Nachdem die Rasterelektronenmikroskopie in fast alle Wissenschaftsbereiche Eingang gefunden hat und die erste Auflage dieses Einführungsbuches relativ schnell vergriffen war, hat sich der Verlag zu einer Neuauflage entschlossen. Die jetzt fertiggestellte, zweite, verbesserte Fassung trägt dem technischen Fortschritt Rechnung und berücksichtigt möglichst viele Anregungen aus dem Kollegenkreis sowie eigene Erfahrungen. So wurde der Textteil durch eine größere Anzahl von *Schemazeichnungen* ergänzt, die Kapitel *Sekundärelektronenemission*, *Auflösungsvermögen* und *Präparationstechnik* auf vielfachen Wunsch ausführlicher behandelt und ein neuer Abschnitt über *Strahlerzeugungssysteme* eingefügt. Der nachfolgende Bildteil wurde durch ergänzendes *Bildmaterial* erweitert, wenige Abbildungen ausgetauscht.

Im *Literaturverzeichnis* konnten viele neue REM-Publikationen aufgenommen werden.

Trotz aller Ergänzungen der Neuauflage hat sich der grundlegende Charakter des Buches nicht geändert. Wir haben uns bewußt auf eine qualitative Beschreibung der physikalischen Grundlagen beschränkt und auf jegliche Formelsprache verzichtet. Das Buch soll auch weiterhin eine leicht lesbare Einführung in die Rasterelektronenmikroskopie bleiben, um Interessenten aus dem Bereich der Biowissenschaften zu zeigen, wie ein Rasterelektronenmikroskop arbeitet und was man von der Rasterelektronenmikroskopie erwarten kann.

Zweifellos würde es den Rahmen eines solchen Buches sprengen, wollte man darüber hinaus alle aktuellen Forschungsergebnisse, die mit dem Rasterelektronenmikroskop erzielt wurden, darstellen. Hier sei auf spezielle Sammelbände, das erwei-

Preface to the second edition

Now that the scanning electron microscope has established itself in almost every field of scientific work, and our introduction to this subject, though published a relatively short while ago, is out of print, our publishers have decided to issue a new edition.

In view of the technical development which had taken place since the publication of the first edition it was natural that we should take this opportunity to revise and supplement its contents. In doing so we have taken advantage of the additional experience we had gained in the meantime, and, wherever possible, we have adopted the numerous suggestions received from scientists working in the same and related fields. Accordingly the text has been supplemented by several *schematic drawings;* the chapters on *secondary electron emission, resolution* and *preparation techniques* have been enlarged in response to many requests; and a chapter on *electron guns* has been added. At the same time a number of *micrographs* have been added to the pictorial section – though a few which appeared in the first edition have now been omitted – and many recent publications on SEM have been added to the *bibliography.*

Yet, despite the inclusion of so much new material, the fundamental character of the book has not changed. Our intention being that it should remain an easily comprehensible introduction to scanning electron microscopy, designed primarily to acquaint those working in the biological sciences with the principles of the microscope and opportunities offered by the investigation technique, we have again deliberately confined ourselves to a qualitative description of the physical facts and have dispensed entirely with mathematical formulae. To have included even a brief survey of all recent research work done with the scanning electron microscope would, without doubt, have taken us far beyond the scope of our main purpose. Those wanting more information on the results of such research are therefore advised to consult the extended bibliography. We would also draw their attention to the detailed mono-

terte Literaturverzeichnis sowie auf Fachtagungen verwiesen.

Wir danken allen Kollegen, die uns ergänzendes Bildmaterial für diese zweite Auflage zur Verfügung gestellt haben. Auch diesmal konnten die Autoren dank des freundlichen Entgegenkommens der Bayer AG, Leverkusen, auf das dortige umfangreiche Bild- und Erfahrungsmaterial zurückgreifen. Wir danken den Mitarbeitern der Bayer AG, die uns Untersuchungsobjekte und -ergebnisse zur Verfügung stellten und uns zum Teil auch bei der Präparation behilflich waren. Dem Georg Thieme Verlag, Stuttgart, insbesondere Herrn Dr. G. HAUFF, danken wir erneut für die übersichtliche Anordnung und gute Ausstattung des Buches. Für die Übertragung des Manuskriptes in die englische Sprache konnte diesmal Herr J. YEO, Leverkusen, gewonnen werden.

Möge die Rasterelektronenmikroskopie auch in den nächsten Jahren für die Grundlagenforschung und Lehre in Medizin und Biologie wie bisher an Bedeutung gewinnen.

Köln/Leverkusen, im März 1978

J. OHNSORGE, R. HOLM

graphs and to the proceedings of conferences.

We wish to thank the many colleagues who have provided us with additional diagrams and micrographs for this edition, and, in particular, Bayer AG, Leverkusen, for allowing us to make use of their large data and micrograph collections. Our thanks are also due to all those at Bayer AG who provided us with specimens and scientific results, and helped us with preparation techniques in some cases. Finally, we would like to express our gratitude to our publishers, the Georg Thieme Verlag, Stuttgart, and especially to Dr. G. HAUFF, for preserving the clear layout and excellent reproduction which already distinguished the first edition, and to Mr. Julian YEO, Leverkusen, who translated the manuscript into English on this occasion.

We hope that in the coming years scanning electron microscopy will continue to make an increasing contribution to basic research and teaching in the spheres of medicine and biology.

Cologne/Leverkusen, March 1978

J. OHNSORGE, R. HOLM

Vorwort zur 1. Auflage

Die Rasterelektronenmikroskopie wird in den nächsten Jahren für die Grundlagenforschung in Medizin und Biologie zunehmend an Bedeutung gewinnen. Die Autoren haben daher versucht, in diesem Buch die wichtigsten Grundlagen der Rasterelektronenmikroskopie zusammenfassend darzustellen.

Wer sich heute in dieses neue Arbeitsgebiet einlesen will, wird bald feststellen, daß in den zahlreichen neueren Publikationen und auf Fachtagungen überwiegend Spezialfragen wie z. B. die Weiterentwicklungen in der Gerätetechnik, spezielle Präparationsmethoden und neueste Untersuchungsergebnisse diskutiert werden, ohne daß jeweils auf die Grundlagen der Rasterelektronenmikroskopie eingegangen wird. Diese Grundlagen sind in verschiedenen Publikationen und zum Teil in Zeitschriften, die nicht zur normalen Ausstattung einer medizinischen Bibliothek gehören, veröffentlicht worden. Aus diesem Grunde wurde nun eine kurze zusammenfassende Einführung in die Rasterelektronenmikroskopie erstellt und durch Bildmaterial ergänzt. Die Lektüre des Buches soll den interessierten Leser in die Lage versetzen, die Fachliteratur verfolgen und eigene Arbeiten aufnehmen zu können. Das vorliegende kleine Buch kann schon vom Umfang her kein Handbuch der Rasterelektronenmikroskopie sein, sondern soll zu den heute vielerorts diskutierten Problemen sowohl geräte- als auch präparationstechnischer Art hinführen.

Dieses Buch ist das Ergebnis einer engen, langjährigen Zusammenarbeit zwischen einem Mediziner und einem Physiker. Dank des freundlichen Entgegenkommens der Bayer AG, Leverkusen, konnten die Autoren auf einen Bildschatz von rund 30 000 rasterelektronenmikroskopischen Aufnahmen zurückgreifen. Wir danken den Mitarbeitern der Bayer AG, die uns Objekte zur Untersuchung zur Verfügung stellten und die uns zum Teil bei der Präparation behilflich waren.

Herrn Prof. Dr. G. PFEFFERKORN und Mitarbeitern, Münster, Herrn Dr. I.-E. RICHTER, Mainz, sowie Herrn Prof. Dr. C.

Preface to the first edition

Since scanning electron microscopy is likely to be of increasing importance for basic research in medicine and biology, the authors have attempted to outline the important basic principles.

Those who wish to familiarise themselves with this new field will soon find themselves confronted with the following difficulty: Most publications and conferences deal mainly with specialised subjects and the latest results of research (e. g. the further advances in instrumental development, specialised techniques of preparation etc.) without discussing the basic principles of scanning electron microscopy. These are given in a variety of publications and in journals which are not normally part of a medical library. It is for this reason that we are providing here a short illustrated introduction to scanning electron microscopy. Studying this book should enable the reader to follow the relevant literature and to start his own research work. This book is not intended to be a comprehensive manual of scanning electron microscopy but should serve as a guide to the main principles of instrument operation and specimen preparation techniques.

The book is the result of many years' close collaboration between a doctor of medicine and a physicist. Bayer AG, Leverkusen, kindly provided access to some 30,000 scanning electron micrographs from which the authors could select appropriate illustrations. We are grateful to our colleagues at Bayer AG for providing us with specimens and assisting with preparation techniques.

We thank Prof. Dr. G. PFEFFERKORN and his co-workers in Münster, Dr. I.-E. RICHTER in Mainz, and Prof. Dr. C. ORFANOS

ORFANOS, Köln, danken wir für die freundliche Überlassung ergänzenden Bildmaterials.

Unser Dank gilt nicht zuletzt dem Verlag Georg Thieme, Stuttgart, insbesondere Herrn Dr. G. HAUFF, für die gute Ausstattung und den klaren Satz des Buches sowie Herrn Dr. L. S. MICHAELIS, Soulbury, und Herrn S. F. H. FLETCHER, Köln, für die sicher nicht immer einfache Übertragung des Manuskriptes in die englische Sprache.

Möge die eindrucksvolle Schärfentiefe der rasterelektronenmikroskopischen Bilder den Leser begeistern und ermuntern, sich selbst mit der Rasterelektronenmikroskopie zu beschäftigen.

Köln/Leverkusen, im August 1973

J. OHNSORGE, R. HOLM

in Cologne, for permitting us to use additional illustrations.

Finally we wish to thank the publisher, Georg Thieme, Stuttgart, in particular Dr. G. HAUFF, for the clear layout and excellent reproduction of the book and also Dr. L. S. MICHAELIS, Soulbury, and Mr. S. F. H. FLETCHER, Cologne, for the by no means easy translation into English.

We hope that the impressive depth of focus of the scanning electron micrographs will evoke the enthusiasm of the reader and encourage him to work in the field of scanning electron microscopy.

Cologne/Leverkusen, August 1973

J. OHNSORGE, R. HOLM

Inhaltsverzeichnis

Contents

Einleitung

Mikroskope dienen in Medizin und Biologie der Aufklärung der Mikromorphologie. Besonders im Bereich der Grundlagenforschung konnten mit ihrer Hilfe viele neue Erkenntnisse gewonnen werden.

Mikroskopie und Biowissenschaften stehen in enger Wechselbeziehung zueinander. Dies wurde bei der Entwicklung der Durchstrahlungselektronenmikroskopie besonders deutlich: Der gerätetechnische Fortschritt führte fast immer auch zu Erfolgen in der biomedizinischen Forschung. Diese Erfolge rechtfertigten einerseits den technischen Aufwand und gaben andererseits neue Anregungen für Physiker und Ingenieure. Man darf davon ausgehen, daß diese Wechselbeziehung in Zukunft auch die Rasterelektronenmikroskopie einschließt.

Eine orientierende mikroskopische Betrachtung eines Objektes wird in der Regel zunächst mit Hilfe eines *Lichtmikroskopes* durchgeführt. Mit dem *Durchstrahlungselektronenmikroskop* können Dünnschnitte und Objektabdrücke differenzierter Oberflächenstrukturen bis in den Sub-nm-Bereich hinein studiert werden. Unbefriedigend blieb bisher jedoch besonders bei höheren Vergrößerungen des Lichtmikroskops die Schärfentiefe der Abbildungen. Räumliche Strukturen können im Lichtmikroskop nur durch Variation der Schärfeneinstellung und im Durchstrahlungselektronenmikroskop durch Auswertung von Serienschnitten näher untersucht werden. Mit dem *Rasterelektronenmikroskop* wurde nun die Darstellung der dritten Dimension in einem zweidimensionalen Bild für einen weiten Vergrößerungsbereich möglich.

Neben den verschiedenen Lichtmikroskopen und dem Durchstrahlungselektronenmikroskop ist seit 1965 das *Rasterelektronenmikroskop* (REM) als weiterer Mikroskoptyp auf dem Markt. Dieses neuartige Elektronenmikroskop wurde zunächst in der physikalischen und chemischen Grundlagenforschung zur Untersuchung rauher Bruch- und anderer Oberflächen mit großem Erfolg eingesetzt, da es Abbildungen mit etwa 300mal größerer Schär-

Introduction

In both medicine and biology, microscopes are used to study micromorphological structures. With their help a great deal of new information has been obtained, particularly in the field of the basic sciences.

Microscopy and the biological sciences are closely interrelated. This has been particularly apparent in the development of transmission electron microscopy, where progress in instrumentation has almost always led to advances in knowledge, while these have not merely justified the technical effort expended, but have, in turn, stimulated physicists and engineers. It seems reasonable to assume that the benefits of this two-way relationship will be extended in the future to the related technique of scanning electron microscopy.

An orientating investigation of a specimen usually starts with the low magnification of a *light optical microscope*. The *transmission electron microscope* has enabled us to examine thin sections and replicas of differentiated surface-structures down to sub nm size. In light microscopy, however, the depth of focus continues to be unsatisfactory, especially at high magnification. To investigate three-dimensional structures with the light microscope it is necessary to vary the focus; with the transmission electron microscope, serial sections are required. The *scanning electron microscope* now permits nearly three-dimensional representation of the object on a two-dimensional picture over a wide range of magnification.

In addition to various light microscopes and the transmission electron microscope, a *scanning electron microscope* (SEM) has been available since 1965. This new type of electron microscope was used originally with great success in physical and chemical research for examination of rough fractures and other surface contours, since the depth of focus is improved 300 times

fentiefe und mindestens 10mal besserem Auflösungsvermögen als das Lichtmikroskop liefert. Aus den gleichen Gründen werden mit dem REM auch *dem Mediziner und Biologen neue Möglichkeiten erschlossen,* da nun auch hier die Oberfläche einer räumlichen Struktur im REM untersucht und damit als Informationsquelle herangezogen werden kann (Abb. 1).

Das REM wird weder das Lichtmikroskop noch das Durchstrahlungselektronenmikroskop verdrängen, sondern diese *klassischen Untersuchungsverfahren vorteilhaft ergänzen.* Nur mit dem Lichtmikroskop sind zur Zeit *farbige* Gewebeaufnahmen möglich. Wird dagegen *höchste mikroskopische Auflösung* bis hin zu 0,1 nm (1 nm = 10^{-6} nm = 10 Å) verlangt, so ist bisher das Durchstrahlungselektronenmikroskop unübertroffen. Sollen jedoch Proben untersucht werden, die weder Abdruck- oder Dünnschnittechniken zulassen noch direkt durchstrahlt werden können, so eröffnet das REM mit seiner ungewöhnlichen Schärfentiefe bisher nicht vorhandene Untersuchungsmöglichkeiten.

Wegen der *Schärfentiefe* wird man in einigen Fällen das REM dem Lichtmikroskop auch dann vorziehen, wenn letzteres zwar die geforderte Vergrößerung noch leistet, das REM jedoch die *räumlichen Strukturen* wesentlich anschaulicher darstellen kann. Es wird daher auch interessant sein, histologische Fragen, die mit dem Lichtmikroskop bereits gelöst wurden, mit dem REM noch einmal zu bearbeiten. Auch die hervorragenden Möglichkeiten des REM als *Kommunikationsmittel,* speziell für Unterrichtszwecke und zur eleganten Demonstration differenzierter räumlicher Strukturen, dürften in Zukunft noch an Bedeutung gewinnen.

Die Anwendung des REM *beschränkt sich jedoch nicht nur auf die Abbildung von Oberflächen.* Durch einfache apparative Zusätze lassen sich die verschiedenen Wechselwirkungen zwischen Elektronen und Materie auch zur Materialdifferenzierung und Analyse der zuvor plastisch abgebildeten Oberfläche ausnutzen. Damit steht ein Gerät zur Verfügung, mit dem die *Oberflächenstruktur* und die *elementare Zusammensetzung dieser Oberflächen* untersucht werden können.

and resolution at least ten times as compared with the light microscope. For the same reason, the SEM *provides new facilities in medical and biological research,* as it permits examination of the surface of a three-dimensional structure with relative ease (Fig. 1a), adding to the information hitherto available.

The SEM will replace neither the light microscope nor the transmission electron microscope but *will offer additional advantages. Color photography,* at present, is only possible with the light microscope; where the *highest power of microscopic resolution* down to 0.1 nm (1 nm = 10^{-6} nm = 10 Å) is required, the transmission electron microscope remains supreme. When, however, specimens are to be examined which do not lend themselves to thin sectioning or replication, the SEM opens up new paths of investigation through its unusual depth of focus.

Because of this *depth of focus,* the SEM is preferable in some cases to the light microscope, which, though it might be able to achieve the magnification required, is unable to give equally good *three-dimensional presentation of structures.* Histological problems which appear to have been solved with the light microscope therefore merit reinvestigation with the SEM. The value of the SEM as a *means of communication,* especially for teaching and demonstration purposes, is being increasingly recognized.

The use of the SEM, however, is *not restricted to the imaging of surfaces.* Additional accessories make it possible to utilize various interactions between the electron beam and the specimen material for various physical analyses of the prepared surface. Thus we approach fulfilment of the concept of possessing an instrument for studying the *topography* of a sample and, in addition, obtaining an *elemental analysis* of the composition of the sample.

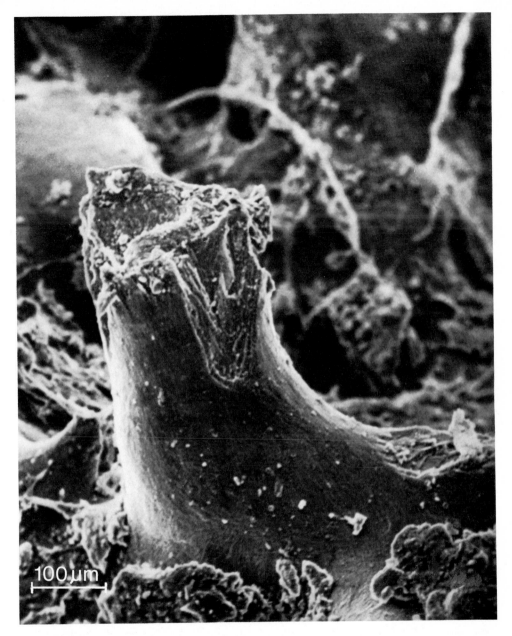

Abb. 1. Rasterelektronenmikroskopische Darstellung eines gebrochenen Spongiosabälkchens des Hüftkopfes.

Fig. 1. Scanning electron microscopic picture of a broken spongiosa trabecula of the femoral head.

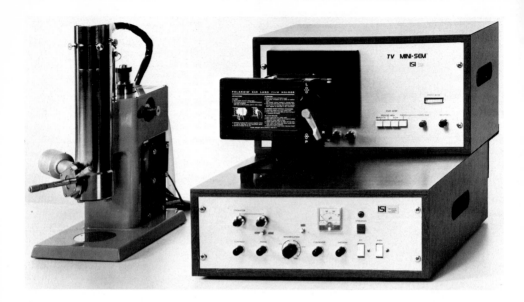

Abb. 2. Rasterelektronenmikroskop „TV Mini-SEM" (International Scientific Instruments). *Einfaches Tischgerät* mit einem Auflösungsvermögen von mehr als 50 nm.
Links: Elektronenoptische Säule.
Rechts: Bedienungskonsole mit Polaroidkamera.

Fig. 2 The "TV Mini-SEM" (International Scientific Instruments). This is a *simple bench instrument* with a resolution better than 50 nm.
Left: Electron-optical column.
Right: Control console with polaroid camera.

Entwicklung des Rasterelektronenmikroskops

Die Grundprinzipien des Rasterelektronenmikroskops wurden von dem deutschen Physiker MAX KNOLL 1935 erkannt. MANFRED VON ARDENNE baute bereits 1938 das erste Rasterelektronenmikroskop, allerdings für Durchstrahlungsexperimente. Unabhängig davon hatte bereits die Entwicklung des heute üblichen Durchstrahlungselektronenmikroskops begonnen. Dieses hatte 1938 einen so hohen Leistungsstand erreicht, daß vorwiegend die Weiterentwicklung des Durchstrahlungselektronenmikroskops vorangetrieben wurde. Erst die neueren Erkenntnisse auf dem Gebiet der Elektronik und besonders der Fernsehtechnik ermöglichten ungefähr ab 1950 C. W. OATLEY, V. E. COSLETT, A. D. G.

Development of the Scanning Electron Microscope

The fundamental principles on which scanning electron microscopy is based were first recognized by the German physicist MAX KNOLL (1935). MANFRED VON ARDENNE (1938) constructed the first SEM; he used it, however, for transmission experiments. The development of the now commonly used transmission electron microscope had already started independently of this. In 1938 the transmission electron microscope had attained such a high standard of efficiency that its further development received first priority. The progress of the modern transmission electron microscope and advances in the field of electronics, especially in television techniques, enabled C. W. OATLEY, V. E. COSLETT, A. D. G. STEWART et al., around 1950,

Abb. 3. Rasterelektronenmikroskop „Stereoscan 180" (Cambridge Instrument Comp.). *Ausbaufähiges vielseitiges Hochleistungsgerät.*
Links: Elektronenoptische Säule mit Elektronenquelle, elektromagnetischen Linsen und Objektkammer mit Probenbühne, darunter der Pumpstand.
Mitte und rechts: Der schrankförmige Aufbau der Bedienungskonsole mit vollautomatischer Vakuumsteuerung, Rasterelektronik, Signalelektronik, Steuerungs- und Kontrollelementen für Hochspannung und Linsenströme sowie mehrere Bildröhren.

Fig. 3 The "Stereoscan 180" scanning electron microscope (Cambridge Instrument Company), a *versatile and sophisticated instrument.*
Left: Electron-optical column with electron gun, electromagnetic lenses and specimen chamber with specimen stage and vacuum unit.
Center and right: Cabinet-type control console with fully automatic vacuum control, scan generator, signal electronic unit, controls for high voltage and lens currents as well as several monitors.

STEWART u. a., das Rasterverfahren zur Abbildung von Oberflächen wieder aufzunehmen und die Grundidee von M. KNOLL und M. VON ARDENNE in Form eines serienreifen Rasterelektronenmikroskops technisch zu verwirklichen.

In jüngster Zeit scheint das Rasterverfahren auch die Durchstrahlungselektronenmikroskopie zurückzuerobern. A. V. CREWE erkannte, daß das Rastertransmissionselektronenmikroskop (STEM = Scanning Transmission Electron Microscopy) gegenüber dem herkömmlichen Durchstrahlungselektronenmikroskop eine Reihe von Vorteilen bietet (z. B. Wegfall des chromatischen Fehlers, leichtere Signalverarbeitung, Energieanalyse der Elektronen). Es gelang ihm, ein Auflösungsvermögen von besser als 0,5 nm zu erreichen und einzelne Schwermetallatome isoliert abzubilden (CREWE u. Mitarb. 1970).

Rasterelektronenmikroskope werden heute von mehr als zehn Firmen hergestellt. Das Angebot reicht von außerordentlich handlichen Tischgeräten bis zu Hochleistungsanlagen mit vielen Zusätzen für Spezialuntersuchungen (Abb. 2–5).

to return to the scanning technique for imaging surface detail and to put into practice the original ideas of M. KNOLL and M. VON ARDENNE.

In the last few years it has become apparent that the scanning technique is also winning back the field of transmission microscopy. A. V. CREWE recognized that the scanning transmission electron microscope (STEM) has several advantages over the conventional transmission electron microscope, such as the absence of the chromatic aberration, easier processing of signals, and energy analysis of the electrons. He obtained a resolution better than 0.5 nm and succeeded in photographing single heavy metal atoms (CREWE et al. 1970).

Scanning electron microscopes are now manufactured by more than ten companies. The range of instruments available extends from highly convenient table units to very powerful ones with many accessories for special investigations (Fig. 2–5).

Abb. 4. Rasterelektronenmikroskop „Stereoscan 600" (Cambridge Instrument Comp.). Ein typi- ▷
sches *Gerät der mittleren Preisklasse.*
Links: Elektronenoptische Säule.
Mitte: Bedienungskonsole mit vereinfachter Elektronik.
Rechts: Bedienungskonsole mit Elektronik zu einem energiedispersiven Röntgenspektrometer (das Spektrometer selbst befindet sich hinter der elektronenoptischen Säule).

Fig. 4. The "Stereoscan 600" scanning electron microscope (Cambridge Instrument Company). A typical *instrument in the medium price range.*
Left: Electron-optical column.
Center: Control console with simplified electronic units.
Right: Control console with electronic unit for an energy dispersive x-ray spectrometer (the spectrometer itself is behind the electron-optical column).

Abb. 5. *Feldemissions-Rasterelektronenmikroskop „HFS-2"* (Hitachi). ▷
Links: Elektronenoptische Säule mit zusätzlichen Pumpen in Höhe des Kathodenraumes.
Rechts: Bedienungskonsole mit mehreren Bildröhren.

Fig. 5. The "HFS-2" *field emission scanning electron microscope* (Hitachi).
Left: Electron-optical column with additional pumps at the height of the cathode compartment.
Right: Control console with several monitors.

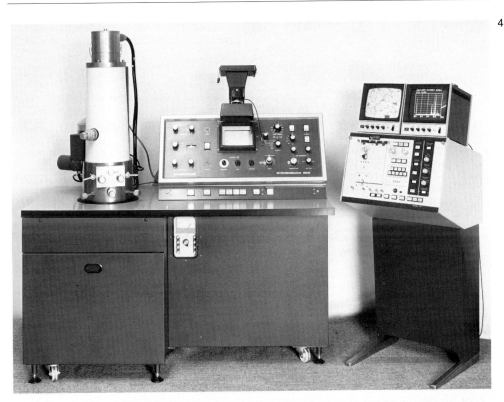

4

5

8

Aufbau eines Rasterelektronen-mikroskops

Ein REM besteht aus einem elektronen-optischen Stand und einer schrankförmigen Bedienungskonsole (s. Abb. 2–5). Der *elektronenoptische Stand* (Abb. 6) ähnelt äußerlich dem Durchstrahlungselektronenmikroskop. Er enthält in einem säulenförmigen Mantel eingebettet die Elektronenquelle, elektromagnetische Linsen zur Bündelung und Spulen zur Ablenkung des Elektronenstrahles sowie die Objektkammer mit Probenbühne und Detektorsystem. Die elektronenoptische Säule mit Objektkammer wird zum Betrieb auf mindestens 10^{-3} Pa* evakuiert, um eine hinreichend große freie Weglänge der Elektronen zu gewährleisten.

An der *Bedienungskonsole* fallen die Leuchtschirme zur Beobachtung und zur photographischen Dokumentation des rasterelektronenmikroskopischen Bildes auf. Weiter sind in der Bedienungskonsole die vollautomatische Vakuumsteuerung, die Rasterelektronik, die Signalelektronik sowie Steuerungs- und Kontrollelemente für Hochspannung und Linsenströme untergebracht (s. Abb. 2–5).

Das zu untersuchende *Objekt* sollte bei Benutzung der Standardbühne (z. B. Abb. 7) eine Größe von etwa 1 cm³ nicht überschreiten. Es wird auf einem gut pfenniggroßen, kreisrunden *Objektteller* (Abb. 7 und 8) fixiert, mit dem eine X-, Y-, Z-Verschiebung, eine Rotation und eine Kippung durchgeführt werden können (Abb. 9). Soll die eingestellte Oberfläche bei Rotation und Kippung stets im Fokus bleiben, so muß die Probenbühne als Goniometertisch (s. Abb. 41) ausgeführt werden. Auch andere Spezialbühnen, z. B. für größere Objekte, sind möglich.

Außer der Probenbühne nimmt die *Objektkammer* die Detektoren für die verschiedenen Wechselwirkungen zwischen Elektronen und Materie auf, die zur Abbildung herangezogen werden können. Säule und Objektkammer sind fest miteinander verbunden und sollen möglichst schwingungsfrei aufgestellt werden. Hierbei müssen noch schärfere Anforderungen als in der Durchstrahlungselektronenmikroskopie gestellt werden, da der Ab-

Construction of a Scanning Electron Microscope

The SEM consists of an *electron-optical column* (Fig. 6) and a cabinet-type control console. The column is outwardly similar to that of the transmission electron microscope. Within the column are an electron gun, electromagnetic lenses for demagnification of the electron beam diameter, and deflection coils. At the base of the column are a specimen chamber, specimen stage and detector system. The electron-optical column with the specimen chamber has to be evacuated to at least 10^{-3} Pa* to achieve long enough mean free pathways for electrons.

The *control console* contains the fluorescent display screens for observation and photographic recording of the image. The console also contains fully automatic control circuits for the vacuum system, the scanning and video processing circuits and controls for EHT and lens currents (Fig. 2–5). When a standard stage (such as that shown in Fig. 7) is used, the *specimen* may be as large as 1 cm³. It is fixed on a slightly larger circular *specimen stub* (Fig. 7, 8), which permits movement in the X, Y and Z planes, with additional rotation and tilting (Fig. 9). If the surface under observation is to remain in focus during rotation and tilting, a "goniometer" type specimen stage (Fig. 41) must be used. Special stages for larger specimens are available.

The *specimen chamber* also contains the detectors utilized to provide information of the various imaging modes available. The specimen chamber and column are firmly connected to each other and should be installed at a site with the lowest possible vibration. As the distance between the

---

* 1 Torr = 1.33×10^2 Pascal (Pa)

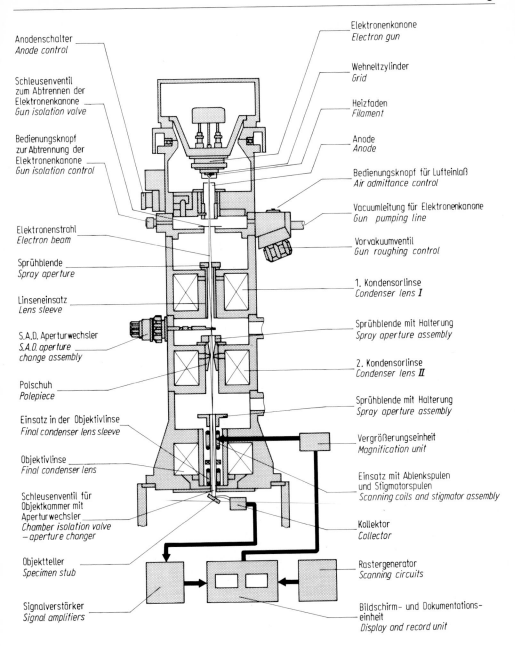

Anodenschalter
Anode control

Schleusenventil
zum Abtrennen der
Elektronenkanone
Gun isolation valve

Bedienungsknopf
zur Abtrennung der
Elektronenkanone
Gun isolation control

Elektronenstrahl
Electron beam

Sprühblende
Spray aperture

Linseneinsatz
Lens sleeve

S.A.D. Aperturwechsler
*S.A.D. aperture
change assembly*

Polschuh
Polepiece

Einsatz in der Objektivlinse
Final condenser lens sleeve

Objektivlinse
Final condenser lens

Schleusenventil für
Objektkammer mit
Aperturwechsler
*Chamber isolation valve
– aperture changer*

Objektteller
Specimen stub

Signalverstärker
Signal amplifiers

Elektronenkanone
Electron gun

Wehneltzylinder
Grid

Heizfaden
Filament

Anode
Anode

Bedienungsknopf für Lufteinlaß
Air admittance control

Vacuumleitung für Elektronenkanone
Gun pumping line

Vorvakuumventil
Gun roughing control

1. Kondensorlinse
Condenser lens I

Sprühblende mit Halterung
Spray aperture assembly

2. Kondensorlinse
Condenser lens II

Sprühblende mit Halterung
Spray aperture assembly

Vergrößerungseinheit
Magnification unit

Einsatz mit Ablenkspulen
und Stigmatorspulen
Scanning coils and stigmator assembly

Kollektor
Collector

Rastergenerator
Scanning circuits

Bildschirm- und Dokumentations-
einheit
Display and record unit

Abb. 6. *Elektronenoptische Säule* des Rasterelektronenmikroskops „Stereoscan S4–10" (Cambridge Instrument Comp.).

Fig. 6. *Electron-optical column* of the "Stereoscan S4–10" scanning electron microscope (Cambridge Instrument Comp.).

Abb. 7. Standardproben-
bühne zum REM „Stereo-
scan 180", daneben
Präparathalter und Test-
objekt (Ag-Gitter).

Fig. 7. Standard speci-
men stage of the "Ster-
eoscan 180" scanning
electron microscope,
with the specimen stub
and test specimen (Ag
grid).

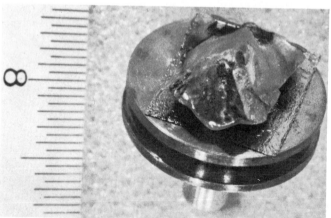

Abb. 8. Probenteller mit
Objekt (Teil eines Zah-
nes).

Fig. 8. Specimen stub
with object (part of a
tooth).

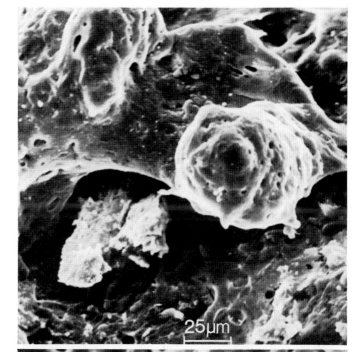

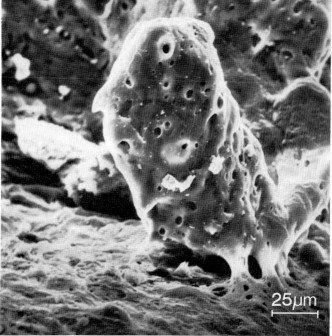

Abb. 9a. Papillenförmiger Knochenzementzapfen (Polymethylmethacrylat) von oben gesehen.

Fig. 9a. Bone cement plug (polymethylmethacrylate), seen from the top.

Abb. 9b. Gleicher Knochenzementzapfen wie Abb. 9 a, seitlich gesehen nach Kippung des Probentellers um 90 Grad.

Fig. 9b. Same bone cement plug as in Fig. 9a, seen after rotation through 90°.

stand zwischen Objektivlinse und Objekt beim REM größer ist als beim Durchstrahlungselektronenmikroskop. Magnetische Wechselfelder sollten am Aufstellungsort des elektronenoptischen Standes kleiner als 5 m Gauß sein.

objective lens and specimen is greater in the scanning electron microscope than in the transmission electron microscope, the SEM has more stringent installation requirements in this respect. Changes in the magnetic fields at the site of the SEM should be less than 5 milligauss.

Arbeitsweise des Rasterelektronenmikroskops

Operation of the Scanning Electron Microscope

In der evakuierten Säule des elektronenoptischen Standes wird durch thermische Emission oder durch Feldemission ein Elektronenstrahl *(Primärstrahl)* erzeugt und mit Hilfe der elektromagnetischen Linsen zu einem feinen Bündel von besser als 10 nm Durchmesser fokussiert. Dieser Primärelektronenstrahl tastet Punkt für Punkt und Zeile für Zeile die Objektoberfläche ab. Ein zweiter Elektronenstrahl *(Schreibstrahl)* zeichnet ebenfalls punkt- und zeilenweise auf dem Leuchtschirm das rasterelektronenmikroskopische Bild auf (Abb. 10). Beide Elektronenstrahlen werden synchron vom gemeinsamen *Rastergenerator* gesteuert (Abb. 11).

Das *rasterelektronenmikroskopische Bild* entsteht auf dem Leuchtschirm nicht gleichzeitig als ganzes Bild wie in der Licht- und Durchstrahlungselektronenmikroskopie, sondern wird punkt- und zeilenweise zusammengesetzt und kann erst auf einem länger nachleuchtenden Schirm oder über den Weg der Filmbelichtung auf der fertigen photographischen Aufnahme betrachtet werden.

Wegen des ungünstigen Signal-Rausch-Verhältnisses läuft der Schreibstrahl in der Bildröhre des REM wesentlich langsamer als der Schreibstrahl in einem Fernsehgerät. Typische Aufnahmezeiten für eine Photographie des REM-Leuchtschirmes sind 40–100 Sekunden. Eine Verbesserung verspricht man sich von neuen Strahlenerzeugungssystemen (S. 16).

Die *Vergrößerung* ergibt sich aus dem Verhältnis von Leuchtschirmfläche zu abgetasteter Objektoberfläche (Abb. 10). Bei einer Leuchtschirmgröße von 10 cm × 10 cm wird bei zwanzigfacher Vergrößerung ein Objektfeld von 5 mm × 5 mm,

In the evacuated electron-optical column, an electron beam (primary beam) is produced either by thermionic emission or, following the method of A. CREWE, by field emission. This *primary beam* is focused by electromagnetic lenses to a fine spot of less than 10 nm in diameter. It scans, point by point and line by line, the surface of the specimen in a square raster. The *electron beams of the cathode ray tube displays* are synchronized with the primary beam so that they faithfully reproduce the scanning image on the C.R.T. screens (Fig. 10). The primary and display beams are controlled by the same *scan generator* (Fig. 11).

The *SEM picture* on the fluorescent display screen does not normally appear all over the screen at the same time as in light or transmission electron microscopy. It is assembled point by point and line by line and can only be viewed on a long persistence C.R.T. screen or recorded photographically on film. Because of the poor signal-to-noise-ratio, the scan speed or time base of the displays is run more slowly than in television. Typical exposure times for a SEM micrograph lie between 40 and 100 seconds. An improvement is expected to result from the use of new electron guns (see below). Recently, TV-type displays for dynamic observation have become rather common, but they are not yet applicable to high resolution work.

Magnification depends on the ratio between the size of the display screen and the area of specimen surface scanned (Fig. 10). If the screen measures 10 cm × 10 cm, a magnification of 20 × will scan an area of

Abb. 10. Bildanalyse und Bildaufbau nach dem Rasterverfahren.

Fig. 10. Analysis and reconstruction of a picture by the scanning method.

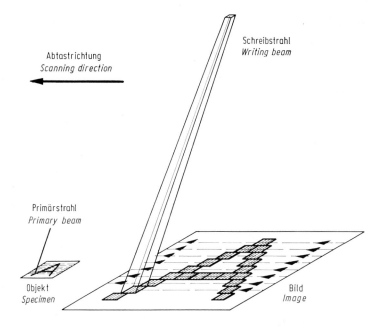

Abtastrichtung
Scanning direction

Schreibstrahl
Writing beam

Primärstrahl
Primary beam

Objekt
Specimen

Bild
Image

Abb. 11. Prinzipbild eines Rasterelektronenmikroskops.

Fig. 11. Block circuit diagram of a scanning electron microscope.

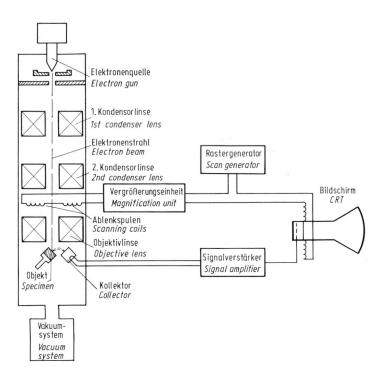

Elektronenquelle
Electron gun

1. Kondensorlinse
1st condenser lens

Elektronenstrahl
Electron beam

2. Kondensorlinse
2nd condenser lens

Vergrößerungseinheit
Magnification unit

Ablenkspulen
Scanning coils

Objektivlinse
Objective lens

Objekt
Specimen

Kollektor
Collector

Vakuumsystem
Vacuum system

Rastergenerator
Scan generator

Bildschirm
CRT

Signalverstärker
Signal amplifier

bei zehntausendfacher Vergrößerung ein Objektfeld von 10 μm × 10 μm abgetastet.

Trifft der Primärelektronenstrahl auf eine Objektoberfläche, so treten eine Reihe von *Wechselwirkungen zwischen Elektronen und Materie auf* (Abb. 12). Im REM wird zur Abbildung der Objektoberfläche die Emission von Sekundärelektronen und von elastisch und inelastisch mit geringem Energieverlust reflektierten Elektronen ausgenutzt. Unter *Sekundärelektronen* faßt man die durch Stoßionisation oder Auger-Effekt von der Substanz emittierten Elektronen zusammen. Die Sekundärelektronen besitzen eine deutlich geringere Energie (0–50 eV) als die Primärelektronen (z. B. 30 000 eV) und die reflektierten Elektronen. Sie werden von einem seitlich angebrachten Kollektor gesammelt (positive Saugspannung) und in der anschließenden Elektronik so verarbeitet, daß *ihre Anzahl die Helligkeit des zugehörigen Bildpunktes auf dem Oszillographenschirm steuert.* Man ist bei diesem Abbildungsverfahren nicht den bekannten Beschränkungen einer Linsenoptik unterworfen. Insbesondere ist die Apertur des Primärstrahls sehr klein (10^{-2}–10^{-3} rad $\triangleq$ 0,6 bis 0,06 °). Man erzielt so eine Schärfentiefe, die etwa 300mal größer ist als beim Lichtmikroskop.

Alle Elektronenmikroskope arbeiten heute mit Elektronenbündeln sehr kleiner Apertur, so daß prinzipiell eine große Schärfentiefe erreicht werden könnte. Diese Eigenschaft kann jedoch im Transmissionselektronenmikroskop nicht voll ausgenutzt werden, da dicke Schichten normalerweise nicht durchstrahlbar und differenziert strukturierte Oberflächen für eine Abdrucktechnik ungeeignet sind. Im REM dagegen wird in der Regel nicht der Abdruck, sondern die Bruch- bzw. Oberfläche direkt abgebildet.

Die Beziehung zwischen Apertur und Schärfentiefe ist in Abb. 13 anschaulich dargestellt. Bei festem Zeilenabstand erscheint das Bild unscharf, sobald Objektbereiche vom Elektronenstrahl mehrfach überstrichen werden, das heißt sobald der gleiche Objektpunkt zur Helligkeit verschiedener Bildpunkte beiträgt. Dies ist bei einem Bündel großer Apertur sehr viel

5 mm × 5 mm; magnification of 10,000 × will scan an area of 10 μm × 10 μm.

When the primary electron beam strikes the surface of a specimen, a number of *interactions between electrons and the material* occur (Fig. 12). For imaging the surface of the specimen in the SEM, we make use of the emission of secondary electrons and of backscattered electrons. *Secondary electrons* are the electrons emitted by the specimen through ionization or the Auger effect. These secondary electrons have considerably less energy (0–50 eV) compared with that of the primary and backscattered electrons (e.g., 30,000 eV). *The electrons are collected* by a laterally placed collector (positively biased), processed electronically, *and used to modulate the brightness of the corresponding image point of the C.R.T. display.* The well-known limitations of lens optics do not apply to this type of image formation. In particular, the illumination aperture of the primary beam is very small (10^{-2}–10^{-3} rad $\triangleq$ 0.6 to 0.06°). This gives a depth of focus about 300 times greater than that obtainable with a light microscope.

All electron microscopes now use electron beams with very small illumination apertures. In principle a large depth of focus should be obtainable, but full use cannot be made of it in the transmission electron microscope as thick sections cannot normally be penetrated and surfaces with rough structures are unsuitable for replication. This does not apply to the SEM, which has been specially designed for direct reproduction of fractures and other surfaces without a need for replica techniques.

Figure 13 clearly shows the relationship between aperture and depth of focus. With the distance between lines fixed, the picture is blurred as soon as parts of the specimen are struck repeatedly by the electron beam, i.e., as soon as the same point of the specimen contributes to the brightness of different points on the screen. This

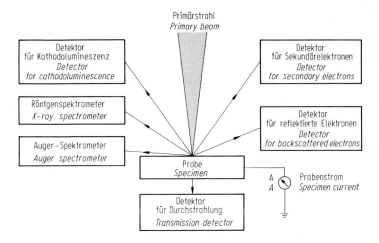

Abb. 12. Möglichkeiten zur *Bilderzeugung und Analyse im REM* aufgrund der verschiedenen *Wechselwirkungen zwischen Elektronen und Materie.*

Fig. 12. Opportunities for *imaging and analysis in the SEM* provided by the various *interactions between electrons and the specimen.*

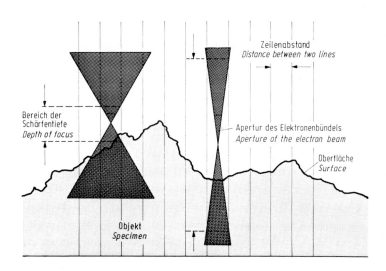

Abb. 13. Schärfentiefe des Rasterelektronenmikroskops.

Fig. 13. Depth of focus in the scanning electron microscope.

häufiger der Fall als bei einem Bündel kleiner Apertur. Im Grenzfall unendlich kleinen Zeilenabstandes tritt an seine Stelle die Größe des Diffusionshofes, aus dem die Sekundärelektronen stammen (vgl. 19 ff.).

is much more common with a spot of large rather than small aperture. In the extreme case of infinitely small distances between the lines, the diffusion halo from which the secondary electrons arise (p. 19) is the limiting factor.

Strahlerzeugungssysteme

Wegen ihrer grundsätzlichen Bedeutung sollen die verschiedenen Möglichkeiten, Elektronenstrahlen für die Rasterelektronenmikroskopie zu erzeugen, etwas eingehender beschrieben werden.

Am gebräuchlichsten ist die *thermische Emission* aus einer *W-Haarnadelkathode.* Man wählt Wolfram (W), weil damit hohe Temperaturen erreicht werden können; außerdem liegt die Austrittsarbeit bei W mit 4,5 eV noch recht günstig im Vergleich mit anderen in Frage kommenden Metallen (z. B. Pt 6,3 eV). Zur Bündelung der emittierten Elektronen dient ein sogenannter Wehneltzylinder, der gegenüber der Kathode sich auf negativem Potential befindet (vgl. Abb. 6 und 11). Dicht vor der Kathode bildet sich der kleinste Strahlquerschnitt, der sogenannte Überkreuzungspunkt (crossover). Er wird mit Hilfe der elektromagnetischen Linsen auf die Probe projiziert und dabei weiter verkleinert. W-Haarnadelkathoden haben eine begrenzte Lebensdauer. Einmal bildet sich mit dem Sauerstoff des Restgases W-oxid, das sublimiert; zum anderen verdampft W auch direkt. Die Folge davon ist, daß der W-Draht dünner wird und schließlich durchbrennt. Die emittierten Elektronen sind nicht monoenergetisch, sondern unterliegen einer Maxwellschen Energieverteilung, deren Breite (0,5 bis 1,5 eV) sich nach den Betriebsbedingungen richtet.

Die *Boride* einiger seltener Erden, z. B. LaB$_6$, haben eine erheblich niedrigere Austrittsarbeit als W und können ebenfalls im Vakuum hoch erhitzt werden (wegen ungenügender Leitfähigkeit meist indirekte Heizung). Deshalb lassen sich mit Kathoden aus diesen Materialien bei gleicher Bündelung höhere Strahlströme als bei W erzielen (Broers 1970).

Electron Guns

In view of their fundamental importance, the various techniques for the production of electron beams for scanning electron microscopy will now be described in some detail.

The technique most commonly used is that of *thermal emission* from a tungsten hairpin cathode. Tungsten (W) is chosen because it enables high temperatures to be reached, and because the work function with W, 4.5 eV, is fairly favorable in relation to the work functions obtained with other metals which might be used (that of Pt, for example, is 6.3 eV). The emitted electrons are collimated by a negatively biased Wehnelt grid (cp. Figs. 6, 11). The smallest beam cross section, the so-called crossover, is situated close to the cathode. It is projected onto the specimen and further reduced at the same time by means of the electromagnetic lenses. The lifetime of a W hairpin cathode is limited, partly because tungsten oxide is formed in a reaction with the oxygen of the residual gas, after which the tungsten oxide is sublimed, and partly because tungsten is also vaporized directly. The tungsten wire therefore becomes thinner, until it finally burns through. The emitted electrons are not monoenergetic, but subject to a maxwellian energy distribution, whose range (0.5–1.5 eV) depends on the operating conditions.

The *borides* of certain rare earths, e.g., LaB$_6$, have considerably lower work functions than W and can likewise be heated to high temperatures in a vacuum (as they are not sufficiently conductive, they generally have to be heated indirectly). Thus, at equal collimation, boride cathodes give higher probe currents than W cathodes do (A. N. Broers 1970).

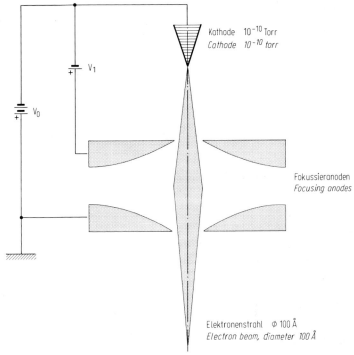

Abb. 14. *Prinzip der Feld-emissionselektronenkanone* nach *Crewe*.

Fig. 14. *Principle of the field emission electron gun* according to *Crewe*.

Kathode 10^{-10} Torr
Cathode 10^{-10} torr

Fokussieranoden
Focusing anodes

Elektronenstrahl $\varnothing$ 100 Å
Electron beam, diameter 100 Å

Die *Feldemission* als Alternative zur thermischen Emission beruht auf dem quantenmechanischen Tunneleffekt. Es sind Feldstärken von mindestens 10^7 V/m erforderlich, die sich an feinen Spitzen (Krümmungsradius etwa 100 nm) leicht erzeugen lassen. Abb. 14 zeigt eine Anordnung, wie sie von CREWE entwickelt wurde. Die spezielle Elektrodenform sorgt neben der Beschleunigung bereits für eine Bündelung der Elektronen. Die Feldemission einer Spitze hängt stark von ihrer kristallographischen Orientierung und von der Kontamination durch Fremdschichten ab. Eine solche Kathode kann deshalb nur unter saubersten Bedingungen stabil arbeiten. *Ultrahochvakuum* (10^{-8} Pa oder besser) ist erforderlich, damit keine Oberflächenbelegungen auftreten und damit keine Ionen aus dem Restgas gebildet werden, die die Spitze beschädigen können. Auch dürfen von den Metallteilen, die von Elektronen getroffen werden (Elektroden, Blenden), keine Ionen abgelöst werden (elektroneninduzierte Ionendesorption), die den gleichen Effekt verursachen. Sind diese Bedingungen erfüllt, so

Field emission, as an alternative to thermal emission, is based on the quantum mechanical tunnel effect. Field strengths of at least 10^7 V/m are needed, but they can be produced easily on fine tips (curvature radius about 100 nm). A corresponding arrangement, developed by CREWE, can be seen in Figure 14. Because of the special shape of the electrodes, the electrons are already focused in addition to being accelerated. The field emission of a tip depends very much on the crystallographic orientation of the tip and on the contamination by extraneous layers. Only if a cathode of this type is kept extremely clean will its performance be stable. An *ultrahigh vacuum* (10^{-8} Pa or lower) is needed to prevent surface contamination and to ensure that no ions, which could damage the tip, are formed from the residual gas. It is also essential that there be no electron-induced ion desorption, i.e., removal of ions, from the metal parts struck by electrons (electrodes and apertures); these ions would have the same effect. The lifetime of a field emission tip is

Tabelle 1 Übersicht zum Vergleich der wichtigsten Strahlerzeugungssysteme (Daten für einen
Arbeitsabstand von 15 mm) (nach *Broers*)
Table 1 *Data for comparison of the main types of electron guns (applicable to a working
distance of 15 mm) (after Broers)*

Kathodentyp	Strahlstrom, für den die Angaben gelten	Strahldurchmesser	Richtstrahlwert	Lebensdauer	Temperatur	Vakuumanforderung (Kathodenraum)
Type of cathode	*Probe current relevant to data in this table*	*Probe diameter*	*Brightness*	*Lifetime*	*Temperature*	*Vacuum required (cathode compartment)*
	A	nm	$\dfrac{A}{cm^2\ ster}$	h	°K	Pascal
W Haarnadel *W hairpin*	10^{-12}	5	10^5	30	2900	10^{-2}
LaB$_6$	10^{-12}	3	10^6	100	2000	10^{-3}
Feldemission (W) *field emission (W)*	10^{-11}	2	10^9	im Idealfall unbegrenzt *unlimited in the ideal case*	RT	10^{-8}

ist die Lebensdauer einer Spitzenkathode praktisch unbegrenzt. Durch geeignetes differentielles Pumpen erreicht man, daß im Bereich der Probenkammer nur die üblichen Vakuumanforderungen gelten müssen.

Die Energieverteilung der Elektronen ist bei Feldemission schärfer als bei thermischer Emission (0,2 eV). Der erzielbare Maximalstrom (ohne Rücksicht auf den Fleckdurchmesser) ist selbstverständlich niedriger, da durch eine feine Spitze nicht beliebig hohe Ströme fließen können, ohne sie zu beschädigen.

In Tab. 1 sind die gebräuchlichsten Strahlerzeugungssysteme zusammengestellt. Eine wichtige Kenngröße für die vergleichende Beurteilung ist der *Richtstrahlwert* (Stromdichte pro Raumwinkeleinheit). Er ist längs der optischen Achse des Gerätes eine Konstante. Je höher der Richtstrahlwert, um so höher ist die Stromdichte in einem gegebenen Strahlquerschnitt. Der Richtstrahlwert ist also von der apparativen Seite her eine maßgebende Größe für das erzielbare Auflösungsvermögen. Bei der Beurteilung der einzelnen Systeme

practically unlimited if these conditions are fulfilled. Suitable differential pumping can ensure that only the normal vacuum requirements need to be maintained in the vicinity of the specimen chamber.

With field emission the energy distribution of the electrons is narrower than in the case of thermal emission (0.2 eV). The highest current obtainable (irrespective of the spot diameter) is, of course, lower, because the current which flows through a fine tip cannot be raised indefinitely without damaging it.

The most commonly used types of electron guns are listed in *Table 1*. An important characteristic of an electron gun is its brightness (current density per solid angle unit), which is constant along the optical axis of the instrument. The higher the brightness, the higher the current density in a given beam cross section. As far as the apparatus is concerned, the brightness is an important measure of the resolution obtainable. When evaluating the individual systems, one should also consider

sollte man jedoch auch den technischen Aufwand (Vakuumanforderung) und die Erzielbarkeit höherer Strahlströme, die z. B. für die Mikroanalyse benötigt werden, berücksichtigen.

Sekundärelektronenemission

Die Sekundärelektronenemission ist der Schlüssel zum richtigen Verständnis der Leistungsfähigkeit eines Rasterelektronenmikroskops und zur Interpretation der damit gewonnenen Bilder (SEILER 1968). Deshalb soll hier etwas ausführlicher darauf eingegangen werden, wenn auch diese physikalischen Überlegungen Medizinern und Biologen zunächst etwas fern liegen. Der Primärstrahl dringt in die Probe ein; durch Streuprozesse werden die Elektronen nach Eintritt in die Probe aus ihrer ursprünglichen Richtung abgelenkt, so daß in einem Probenbereich (in Abb. 15 punktiert gezeichnet) *Wechselwirkungen zwischen Elektronen und Materie* ablaufen. Die bei diesen *Stoß-, Ionisierungs-* bzw. *Auger-Prozessen* freigesetzten Elektronen mit geringer Energie können nur dann die Probenoberfläche verlassen, wenn sie in der Nähe der Oberfläche erzeugt werden. Dagegen können Elektronen, die nur in ihrer Richtung abgelenkt wurden, aber keine nennenswerten Energieverluste erfahren haben, auch aus größerer Tiefe kommend von der Probe ins Vakuum austreten. Sie können zum Bildaufbau beitragen, zumal sie in oberflächennahen Schichten nochmals Sekundärelektronen auslösen.

Betrachtet man die *Energieverteilung der von der Probe emittierten Elektronen* (Abb. 16), so hat diese Kurve zwei ausgeprägte Maxima; eines bei der Energie der Primärelektronen, das zweite bei sehr niedrigen Energien. Das erstere ist zurückzuführen auf die elastisch oder nur mit geringen Energieverlusten *reflektierten Elektronen,* das zweite auf die eigentlichen *Sekundärelektronen.* Diesem Untergrund sind weitere Maxima aufgeprägt, die *Auger*-Übergängen zugeordnet sind, aber meist wegen ihrer geringen Intensität nur mit besonderen elektronischen Hilfsmitteln sichtbar gemacht werden können.

Emission of Secondary Electrons

The emission of secondary electrons is the key to a correct understanding of the opportunities provided by scanning electron microscopy and to an interpretation of the images obtained (H. SEILER 1968). It will therefore be considered here in some detail, even if the relevant physical considerations may at first appear to physicians and biologists to be somewhat remote from their respective disciplines.

After the primary beam has entered the specimen, its electrons are deflected by scattering processes from their original course, with the result that *interactions between electrons and matter* occur in a part of the specimen (indicated by a dotted line in Fig. 15). Electrons of low energy which are liberated by these *impact ionization* and *Auger processes* are only able to leave the surface of the specimen if they are produced near to it. On the other hand, electrons which have merely been deflected, and have not suffered appreciable losses of energy, are able to enter the vacuum, even from considerable depths within the specimen. They contribute to the formation of the image, particularly as they release further secondary electrons in layers close to the surface.

The plot of the *energy distribution of the electrons emitted by the specimen* (Fig. 16) has two pronounced maxima: one at the energy of the primary electrons and the other at very low energies. The first corresponds to the *electrons reflected* elastically, or backscattered with small energy losses only, and the second to the true *secondary electrons.* Superimposed on this background are further maxima, which are associated with *Auger* transitions, but whose intensity is so low that in most cases they can be made visible only with special electronic devices.

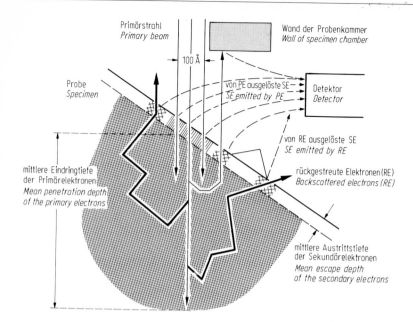

Abb. 15. *Sekundärelektronenemission.* Diese erfolgt einmal vom Auftreffpunkt der Primärelektronen, zum anderen bei der Emission rückgestreuter Elektronen aus dem Bereich der Eindringtiefe (punktierter Bereich) der Primärelektronen in die Probe.

Fig. 15. *Secondary electron emission.* Secondary electrons are produced partly at the point of incidence of the primary electrons and partly by backscattered electrons emitted from the region of the penetration depth of the primary electrons (dotted area).

Abb. 16. Energieverteilung der Sekundärelektronen (schematisch für 30 keV ▷ Primärelektronen), die von einem angeregten Oberflächenbereich emittiert werden. Die Energieverluste und Auger-Linien sind übertrieben gezeichnet.

Fig. 16. Energy distribution of the secondary electrons emitted from an irradiated area of the surface (shown schematically for primary electrons of 30 keV). The energy losses and Auger lines have been emphasized.

Abb. 17. Die Sekundärelektronenausbeute $\delta = \dfrac{\text{SE (Sekundärelektronen)}}{\text{PE (Primärelektronen)}}$ ▷
in Abhängigkeit von der Energie der Primärelektronen (schematisch).

Fig. 17. Secondary electron yield $\delta = \dfrac{\text{SE (secondary electrons)}}{\text{PE (primary electrons)}}$ versus the primary electron energy (schematic representation).

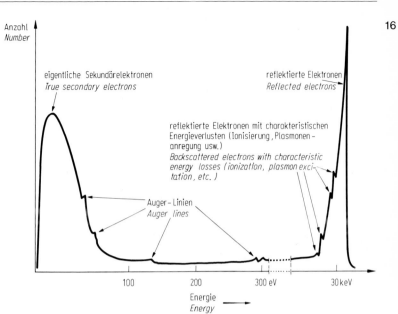

eigentliche Sekundärelektronen
True secondary electrons

reflektierte Elektronen
Reflected electrons

reflektierte Elektronen mit charakteristischen
Energieverlusten (Ionisierung, Plasmonen-
anregung usw.)
*Backscattered electrons with characteristic
energy losses (ionization, plasmon excitation, etc.)*

Auger-Linien
Auger lines

Anzahl
Number

100   200   300 eV   30 keV

Energie
Energy

16

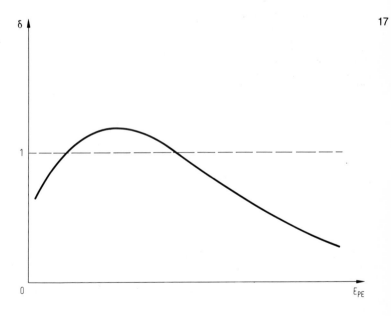

δ

1

0

E_{PE}

17

Die Richtungsverteilung der Sekundärelektronen ist nahezu unabhängig von der Richtung der Primärelektronen, nur bei Einkristallen können sich durch Channeling-Effekte geringe Abweichungen ergeben. Eine Saugspannung führt die Sekundärelektronen auf gekrümmten Bahnen dem Detektor zu; deshalb fehlen im Sekundärelektronenbild ausgeprägte Schatten. Bei den *reflektierten Elektronen* (RE) findet man dagegen eine deutliche Vorwärtsstreuung, die zu Schatten in der Abbildung führt. Die Ausbeute an *Sekundärelektronen* (SE) pro einfallendes *Primärelektron* (PE) am Auftreffpunkt des Primärstrahles ($\delta = \frac{SE}{PE}$) ist die für die Helligkeit des Bildpunktes maßgebliche Größe. Ihre Abhängigkeit von der Energie der Primärelektronen zeigt schematisch Abb. 17. Für jedes Material gibt es ein Maximum der SE-Ausbeute. Dieses liegt für Metalle nur wenig über 1 bei Primärelektronenenergien von 300–800 eV; bei Isolatoren kann δ Werte bis 30 annehmen und der Bereich $\delta > 1$ erstreckt sich bis zu mehreren keV Primärelektronenenergie. Abb. 18a–d zeigt weitere Einflußgrößen. δ nimmt mit der *Neigung der Probe* zu, da bei schrägem Einfall der Primärelektronen auf der Probenoberfläche mehr Sekundärelektronen in oberflächennahen Bereichen erzeugt werden als bei einem senkrechten Einfall der Primärelektronen. Aus dem gleichen Grund erscheinen feine Spitzen besonders hell (*Reliefkontrast*). Die Abb. 19 und 20 zeigen die Verhältnisse an schematischen Objekten. In Abb. 19 gibt es in horizontaler Lage der Probe nur Flächen mit zwei verschiedenen Neigungswinkeln. Dementsprechend ist das SE-Signal eine Rechteckkurve mit nur zwei Werten; ein räumlicher Eindruck entsteht so nicht. Bei Neigung des Objektes um den Winkel α sind die mit gleicher Steigung nach links und rechts geneigten Flächen nicht mehr gleichwertig; dies führt zu einem *räumlichen Eindruck*, gleichzeitig ist die mittlere Bildhelligkeit größer. Auch die *Lage der Probenoberfläche zum Detektor* ist für die Helligkeit der Bildpunkte und damit auch für den räumlichen Eindruck maßgebend. Von Flächenelementen, die dem Detektor abge-

The angular distribution of the secondary electrons is almost independent of the direction of the primary electrons; although where single crystals are concerned, slight deviations may result from channeling effects. An extraction voltage guides the secondary electrons on curved paths to the detector; pronounced shadows are therefore absent from the secondary electron image. On the other hand, there is pronounced forward scattering of the *reflected electrons* (RE), which results in the formation of shadows. The yield of *secondary electrons* (SE) per incident *primary electron* (PE) at the point of incidence of the primary beam ($\delta = \frac{SE}{PE}$) is the quantity on which the brightness of the image point mainly depends. Its dependence on the energy of the primary electrons is shown schematically in Fig. 17. There is a maximum SE yield for every material. The maxima of metals are not much higher than 1 at primary electron energies of 300–800 eV; with insulating materials the value of δ may be up to 30, while the range $\delta > 1$ extends to primary electron energies of several keV. The influences of further quantities can be seen in Fig. 18a–d. The value of δ increases with the *angle of tilting of the specimen* as more secondary electrons are formed in areas near the surface of the specimen when the primary electrons enter the specimen obliquely than when they enter it vertically. That is why fine points appear particularly bright (*relief contrast*). Fig. 19 and 20 demonstrate the relationships for schematically drawn objects. In Fig. 19 every area has two different tilting angles when the specimen is in the horizontal position. The SE signal is, accordingly, a flat-topped curve with only two values; a three-dimensional impression is not formed in this way. After tilting of the object through the angle α, the surfaces equally inclined to the left and right are no longer equivalent; this creates a *three-dimensional impression* and also raises the mean brightness of the image. The *position of the surface of the specimen relative to the detector* also has a decisive influence on the brightness of the image points and hence on the formation of the three-di-

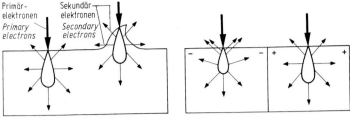

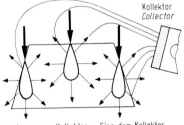

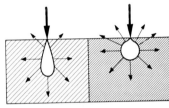

a Oberflächengestalt : Erhebungen sind heller als glatte Flächen

Effect of topography : spikes and edges are brighter than plane surfaces

b Elektrische Ladung : Negativ geladene Stellen sind heller als positiv geladene

Effect of electric charge : negatively charged points are brighter than positively charged ones

c Lage zum Kollektor : Eine dem Kollektor zugewandte Fläche ist heller als eine abgewandte

Effect of position relative to the collector : a surface turned toward the collector is brighter than one turned away from it

d Materialbeschaffenheit : Schwere Elemente sind heller als leichte

Effect of chemical composition : regions of heavy elements are brighter than those of light ones

Abb. 18 a–d. Kontrastentstehung im Rasterelektronenmikroskop.

Fig. 18 a–d. Contrast mechanisms in the scanning electron microscope.

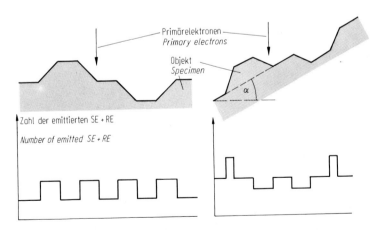

Abb. 19. Abhängigkeit der Zahl der emittierten Sekundärelektronen (SE) und reflektierten Elektronen (RE) vom *Neigungswinkel der Probe.*

Fig. 19. Influence of the *tilting angle of the specimen* on the number of emitted secondary electrons (SE) + reflected electrons (RE).

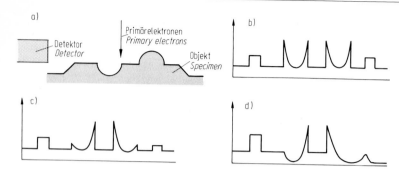

Abb. 20. *Kontrastentstehung* im Rasterelektronenmikroskop.
a) Schematisches Modellobjekt.
b) Zahl der von dieser Objektoberfläche emittierten SE und RE.
c) Zahl der vom Detektor für die einzelnen Flächenelemente nachgewiesenen SE + RE (mit Saugspannung).
d) Zahl der vom Detektor nachgewiesenen RE (ohne Saugspannung erreichen die SE nicht den Detektor).

Fig. 20. *Contrast mechanisms* in the scanning electron microscope.
a) Schematic drawing of a specimen.
b) Number of SE and RE emitted from this surface of the specimen.
c) Number of SE + RE detected (with extraction voltage) for the individual surface elements.
d) Number of RE detected (in the absence of extraction voltage, SE do not reach the detector).

Abb. 21. Beispiel zum *Materialkontrast im REM:* Weichlot auf Eisen. Das Lot ist Pb-haltig und erscheint deshalb hell.

Fig. 21. Example of *atomic number contrast in the SEM:* soft solder on iron. The solder contains lead and therefore appears bright.

wandt sind, gelangen bei gleicher SE-Emission trotz Saugspannung weniger SE in den Detektor als von zugewandten Flächen (s. Abb. 29). Noch ausgeprägter ist der Effekt bei den RE; hier können Objektdetails, die im Schatten liegen, verlorengehen.

Negativ aufgeladene Flächen emittieren mehr SE als positiv aufgeladene. Dieser *Potentialkontrast* kann bei der Untersuchung von Halbleiterproben u. a. zur Messung von Spannungen ausgenutzt werden; sonst macht er sich meist als *Aufladungseffekt* störend bemerkbar. Grundsätzlich sind zwei Arten der Aufladung denkbar: Einmal können mehr Elektronen emittiert werden als Primärelektronen einfallen, die Probe lädt sich positiv auf. Dadurch werden die PE zusätzlich beschleunigt, so daß δ sinkt und ein Gleichgewichtszustand erreicht wird. Sehr viel häufiger ist der Fall, daß mehr PE auf die Probe gelangen als SE und RE emittiert werden, die Probe wird negativ aufgeladen. Dadurch werden die PE gebremst, so daß δ steigt, bis sich ein Gleichgewicht einstellt. Diese Art der Aufladung kann bei guten Isolatoren fast das Potential der PE erreichen. Da die Aufladungen weder räumlich noch zeitlich konstant sind, können sie eine Abbildung der Probe unmöglich machen (d. h. der Potentialkontrast überwiegt den Reliefkontrast); deshalb müssen sie durch geeignete Präparationsmaßnahmen verhindert werden.

Bei den *reflektierten Elektronen* ist vor allem die Materialabhängigkeit der Ausbeute $\eta = \dfrac{RE}{PE}$ hervorzuheben. η steigt mit der Ordnungszahl monoton an. Der *Materialkontrast* ist jedoch in der Regel kleiner als der Reliefkontrast, so daß er nur bei relativ ebenen Proben hervortritt. Als Beispiel zeigt Abb. 21 die Verteilung von Weichlot auf Eisen. Das Lot ist bleihaltig und erscheint deshalb hell.

Da RE auch aus tieferliegenden Probenbereichen austreten können (Reichweite von 50 keV Elektronen in Al etwa 10 µm,

mensional impression. At a given SE emission, despite extraction voltage, fewer SE enter the detector from surface components not facing the detector than from surfaces facing it (see Fig. 29). This effect is still more pronounced with the RE; details of the object which are in shadow may be lost here.

Negatively charged surfaces emit more SE than those charged positively. This *potential contrast* can be utilized in the investigation of semiconductor samples, including the measurement of voltages; otherwise it generally causes disturbances through its *charging effect*. In principle, two types of charging are conceivable. In the one case, the number of electrons emitted is greater than that of the incident primary electrons; the specimen therefore receives a positive charge. This causes additional acceleration of the PE, with the result that δ falls and a state of equilibrium is reached. In the other case, which is much more common, the number of PE reaching the specimen is greater than that of the SE and RE emitted, with the result that the specimen is charged negatively. In this way the PE are retarded so that δ rises until equilibrium is reached. Where good insulators are concerned, charges produced in this way may be almost equal to the potential of the PE. As the charges are constant neither in space nor in time, they may make imaging of the specimen impossible (if the potential contrast is more powerful than relief contrast). Their formation must therefore be prevented by suitable preparation methods.

With regard to the *backscattered electrons,* particular attention is drawn to the dependence on the material of the yield $\eta = \dfrac{RE}{PE}$.

η rises monotonously with the atomic number. As a rule, however, the *material contrast* is less pronounced than the relief contrast and therefore becomes apparent only if the specimen is relatively smooth. As an example, Figure 21 shows the distribution of soft solder on iron. The solder contains lead and therefore appears bright.

As RE are able to emerge from deeper parts of the specimen also (the range of 50-keV electrons is about 10 µm in Al and

a

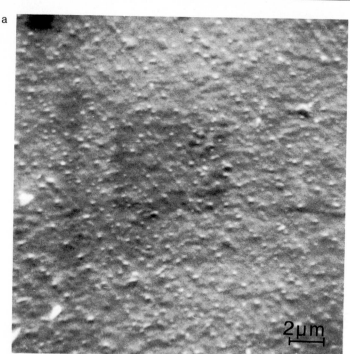

b

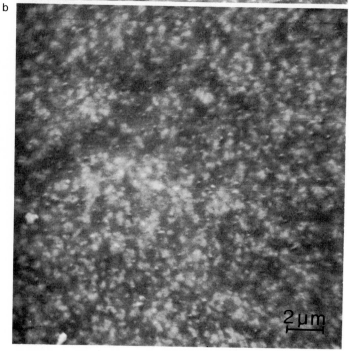

Abb. 22. Beispiel für die Abhängigkeit der *Eindringtiefe der Primärelektronen von der Primärstrahlspannung*. Oberfläche eines pigmentierten Lackes im REM
a) mit 5 kV,
b) mit 20 kV
   Primärstrahlspannung abgebildet.

Fig. 22. Example of the dependence of the *penetration depth of the primary electrons on the primary beam voltage*. Paint surface imaged in the SEM at
a) 5 kV primary beam voltage,
b) 20 kV primary beam voltage.

Abb. 23. *Durchstrahlungs-
effekte* an dünnen Mem-
branen, demonstriert an
einem Schaumstoff.
a) Mit 2 kV Primärstrahl-
spannung ohne Durch-
strahlung der dünnen
Membranen,
b) bei 10 kV Primärstrahlspannung mit deutli-
chen Durchstrahlungs-
effekten abgebildet.

Fig. 23. *Transmission
effects* on thin membranes,
demonstrated by a syn-
thetic foam material.
a) 2 kV primary beam
voltage without trans-
mission through the
thin membranes,
b) 10 kV primary beam
voltage with pro-
nounced transmission
effects.

a

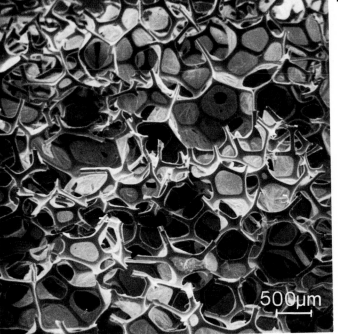

b

in Au etwa 1 µm), ist es möglich, auch nicht direkt an der Oberfläche liegende *Einschlüsse aus schwereren Elementen mit Hilfe des Materialkontrastes abzubilden.* Dies wird deutlich am Beispiel eines pigmentierten Lackes. Abb. 22a wurde mit 5 kV Primärstrahlspannung gewonnen. Es sind nur die Pigmente sichtbar, die aus der Oberfläche herausragen. Bei 20 kV Primärstrahlspannung dominieren dagegen viele unscharfe helle Flecken, die zu Pigmenten in größerer Tiefe gehören (Abb. 22b). Sie erscheinen hell aufgrund des Unterschiedes der mittleren Ordnungszahlen von Pigment und Bindemittel; sie sind unscharf, da die RE aus einem gewissen Bereich um den Auftreffpunkt des Primärstrahles herum austreten können.

Es wird also im REM niemals die Oberfläche im mathematischen Sinn abgebildet, sondern *„man sieht stets etwas in die Probe hinein".* Die erfaßte Tiefe hängt von der Energie der Primärelektronen und von der Dichte des untersuchten Materiales ab (s. Abb. 15).

Da die RE beim Austritt aus der Oberfläche SE auslösen, erscheint der Materialkontrast auch im SE-Bild. Der Beitrag der durch RE ausgelösten SE ist recht erheblich und kann bei Schwermetallen den Anteil der durch die PE ausgelösten SE übertreffen.

Dünne Membranen können von hochenergetischen PE durchstrahlt werden. Es kommt dann auf der Vorder- und der Rückseite der Membran zur Emission von SE. Solche Bereiche des Bildes erscheinen dann besonders hell. Als Beispiel zeigt Abb. 23a und b einen Schaumstoff, der einmal mit 2 kV, zum anderen mit 20 kV Primärstrahlspannung abgebildet wurde. Eine Oberflächenabbildung sollte demnach möglichst mit niedriger Primärstrahlspannung vorgenommen werden.

about 1 µm in Au), *inclusions of heavier elements* that are not situated at the surface itself can likewise be *imaged by means of the material contrast.* This can be seen from the example given in Figure 22a, in which the pigment of a paint was imaged at a primary beam voltage of 5 kV. Only the pigment particles which protrude from the surface are visible. At 20 kV, however, the image is dominated by numerous indistinctly outlined spots belonging to pigment particles at a greater depth (Fig. 22b). Their brightness is explained by the difference between the mean atomic numbers of the pigment and binder; they are indistinctly outlined because the RE are able to emerge from a certain area surrounding the point of incidence of the primary beam.

Thus the SEM never displays the two-dimensional surface of the specimen only; deeper layers may contribute to the picture also. This thickness of the imaged surface layer depends on the energy of the primary electrons and on the density of the material under investigation (Fig. 15).

Since the RE release SE as they emerge from the surface, the material contrast also appears in the SE picture. The contribution of the SE released by RE is considerable, and, where heavy metals are concerned, the number of SE released in this way may exceed the number released by the PE.

High-energy PE are able to pass through thin membranes. SE are then emitted from both sides of the membrane. The corresponding areas of the picture appear particularly bright. A picture of a synthetic foam material imaged at a primary beam voltage of 2 kV in the one case and of 20 kV in the other is reproduced in Fig. 23a and b as an example. Hence, where possible, low primary beam voltages should be used for true surface images.

Auflösungsvermögen

Das Auflösungsvermögen und damit die erzielbare förderliche Vergrößerung hängt sowohl vom untersuchten *Objekt* als auch vom *Gerät* ab. Sekundärelektronen und reflektierte Elektronen werden nicht nur vom Auftreffpunkt des Primärstrahles emittiert, sondern stammen stets auch aus einem gewissen *Diffusionshof um den Auftreffpunkt* herum (s. Abb. 15). Dieser Diffusionshof ist bei Schwermetallen besonders klein; deshalb kann an massiven Schwermetallproben ein besseres Auflösungsvermögen erzielt werden als zum Beispiel an Graphit. An Au kann bei einem Primärstrahldurchmesser von 10 nm ein Auflösungsvermögen von etwa 20 nm erreicht werden. Dies entspricht einer *förderlichen Vergrößerung* von 5000- bis 10 000fach. Arbeitet man mit 1000 Zeilen pro Bild, so erscheint das Bild so lange scharf, wie der Durchmesser des Diffusionshofes kleiner ist als der Zeilenabstand. Dies ist bei 5000facher Vergrößerung noch erfüllt (20 nm entsprechen 0,1 mm). Sieht man eine Bildunschärfe von 0,3 mm noch als tragbar an, so kann man bis 15 000fach sinnvoll vergrößern. Aber auch einer *Verkleinerung des Primärstrahldurchmessers* sind physikalische Grenzen gesetzt. Der Richtstrahlwert der Elektronenkanone ist nicht beliebig hoch; dies führt zum *Signal-Rausch-Verhältnis* als einem limitierenden Faktor. Die fokussierenden Linsen haben *Fehler* (*sphärisch:* Punkt wird als Scheibe abgebildet; *chromatisch:* Brennweite hängt von der Energie der Elektronen ab; *astigmatisch:* Linsenfeld nicht rotationssymmetrisch). Unrunde Blendenbohrungen, falsche Zentrierung von Blenden und Linsen sowie Verschmutzung sorgen für zusätzlichen Astigmatismus, der nur teilweise durch Korrekturlinsen ausgeglichen werden kann. Um in der Probenkammer viel Bewegungsfreiheit zu haben, muß die unterste Linse eine große Brennweite erhalten. Dadurch werden ihre Fehler besonders groß. Ein *Gerät für Höchstauflösung* muß also neben bester mechanischer Schwingungsdämpfung, magnetischer Abschirmung und Brummfreiheit im wesentlichen drei Elemente vereinigen: Elektronenkanonen

Resolution

The resolution, and hence the useful magnification obtainable, depend both on the *object* under investigation and on the *instrument*. Secondary and backscattered electrons are never emitted exclusively from the point of incidence of the primary beam since they always originate, to some extent, from a certain *diffusion zone* surrounding the point of incidence (Fig. 15). This diffusion zone is very small for heavy metals, on samples of which, therefore, better resolution can be achieved than, for example, on graphite. With a primary beam of 10 nm diameter, a resolution of about 20 nm can be obtained on Au. This corresponds to a *useful magnification* of 5000–10,000 ×. If one is working with a raster of 1000 lines per picture, this will remain in focus as long as the diameter of the diffusion zone is smaller than the distance between the lines. This applies up to a magnification of 5000 × (20 nm corresponds to 0.1 mm). If a lack of definition of 0.3 mm is tolerable, a magnification of 15,000 × is possible.

However, there are also physical limits to the extent to which the *primary beam diameter can be reduced*. The brightness of the electron gun cannot be raised indefinitely. Therefore the *signal-to-noise ratio* appears as a limiting factor. The focusing lenses have *aberrations (spherical aberration:* a point appears as a disk; *chromatic aberration:* the focal length depends on the energy of the electrons; *astigmatism:* the lens field is not rotationally symmetrical). Additional astigmatism, which cannot be entirely eliminated with correction lenses, is caused by out-of-round aperture holes, inaccurate centering of apertures and lenses and the presence of dirt. The objective lens must have a long focal length to provide plenty of freedom of movement in the specimen chamber. This, however, increases its aberrations.

Thus, if an instrument is to give the *highest possible resolution,* it must have – in addition to the best possible mechanical vibration damping, magnetic screening and freedom from ripple – three important

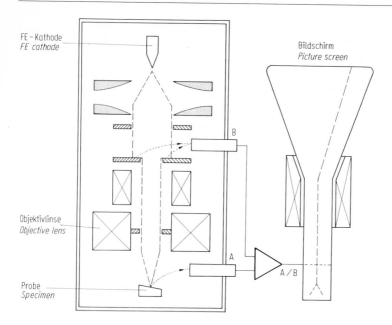

FE – Kathode
FE cathode

Bildschirm
Picture screen

B

Objektivlinse
Objective lens

A

A / B

Probe
Specimen

Abb. 24. Feldemissions-REM mit SE-Detektor A und mit *Referenz-detektor* B. Durch Divisionsbildung der Signale von A und B werden Intensitätsschwankungen, die von der FE-Kathode herrühren, weitgehend ausgeglichen.

Fig. 24. Field emission scanning electron microscope with SE detector A and *reference detector* B. Intensity fluctuations originating from the field emission cathode are largely eliminated by formation of the quotient of signals A and B.

Abb. 25. Höchste Auflösung. Grobe Inhomogenitäten in der Au-Be- ▷
dampfungsschicht auf einem Tonband, aufgenommen mit einem *Feldemissions-REM. (Nagatani* u. *Saito,* Applikationslabor Hitachi Ltd., Japan).

Fig. 25. *Very high resolution.* Pronounced irregularities in the Au vapor layer on a sound recording tape, photographed with a *field emission SEM.*

Abb. 26. T4-Bakteriophagen auf Kolibakterien (unbedampft). ▷
Aufgenommen mit einem Feldemissions-REM (Hitachi HFS-2).
(*Takeya* u. *Amako,* Kyushu Universität, Japan).

Fig. 26. T4-bacteriophages on coli bacteria (uncoated). Photographed with a field emission SEM (Hitachi HFS-2).

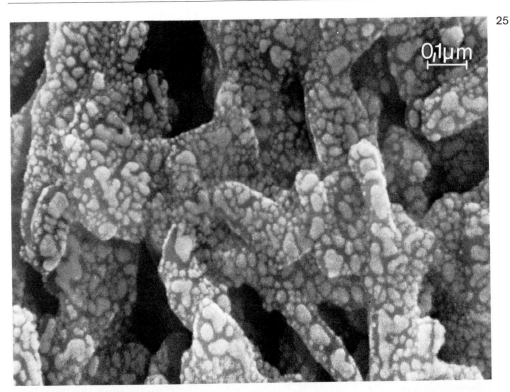

25

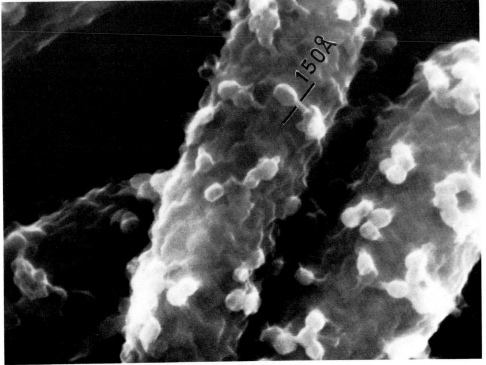

26

mit hohem Richtstrahlwert, kurzbrennweitige unterste Linse und Energiefilterung der RE bzw. SE. Letzteres dient der Beschränkung auf diejenigen RE, die elastisch reflektiert werden und überwiegend vom Auftreffpunkt der PE stammen. In einem nach diesen Gesichtspunkten konstruierten Versuchsgerät (WELLS 1973) konnten BROERS u. Mitarb. (1974) auch an biologischen Objekten ein Auflösungsvermögen von etwa 2 nm erreichen (s. Abb. 94). Die Modifikation der untersten Linse schließt jedoch die Untersuchung voluminöser Proben mit großen Höhenunterschieden aus. Um bei großem Arbeitsabstand wie in einem üblichen REM arbeiten zu können, bleibt wohl nur der Weg, *Feldemissionskathoden* einzusetzen. Um die praktisch unvermeidlichen Emissionsschwankungen zu eliminieren, führten SAITO, TODOKORO, NAMURA und KOMODA einen *Referenzdetektor* ein (Abb. 24); sie steuerten die Helligkeit des Bildpunktes nicht mit dem Signal des Detektors A (üblicher SE-Detektor), sondern verwandten den Quotienten der Signale der Detektoren A und B (Referenzdetektor). Ist eine Änderung des Signales von A auf eine Schwankung des Primärstrahlstromes zurückzuführen, so ändert sich das Signal von B entsprechend und die Quotientenbildung führt zu einem nach wie vor konstanten Signal. Signaländerungen von A infolge Änderungen an der Probe wirken sich dagegen voll auf die Bildhelligkeit aus. Auf diese Weise gelang es, Inhomogenitäten in der Bedampfungsschicht nachzuweisen (Abb. 25) oder Bakteriophagen auf Bakterien abzubilden (Abb. 26).

Von der Möglichkeit, zwei Punkte getrennt wahrzunehmen (*Punktauflösungsvermögen*), ist die Wahrnehmung von Höhenstufen (*Stufenauflösungsvermögen*) zu unterscheiden. Aufgrund der erhöhten SE-Emission an feinen Kanten sind Stufen mit einer Höhendifferenz, die kleiner als der Primärstrahldurchmesser ist, noch erkennbar. Da sie als Strich mit einer Breite, die mindestens dem Primärstrahldurchmesser entspricht, gezeichnet werden, ist hier natürlich eine Messung der Höhendifferenz ausgeschlossen (SCHUR u. Mitarb. 1968).

elements: an electron gun with a high brightness, an objective lens with a short focal length, and an energy filter for the RE or SE. The purpose of the filter is to let through only those RE which are elastically reflected and originate mainly from the point of incidence of the PE. In an experimental instrument designed according to these principles (WELLS 1973), BROERS et al. (1974) achieved a resolution of about 2 nm on a variety of objects, including biological specimens (see Fig. 94). But the modification adopted for the objective lens of this instrument makes it impossible to investigate bulky specimens with rough surfaces. The only way to enable work to be carried out at a large working distance, as it can in a normal SEM, is apparently to use *field emission cathodes.* SAITO, TODOKORO, NAMURA and KOMODA introduced a *reference detector* to eliminate the practically unavoidable emission fluctuations (Fig. 24). They controlled the brightness of the image point not with the signal of detector A (an ordinary SE detector) but with the quotient of the signals of detectors A and B (i.e., by means of a reference detector). If a change in the signal from detector A is caused by a fluctuation in the primary beam current, the signal from detector B changes correspondingly and the quotient formation keeps the signal constant, as it was before. But changes in the signal from detector A resulting from changes in the specimen affect the brightness of the image to the full extent. By means of this technique it has been possible to detect inhomogeneities in vapor coats (Fig. 25) and to photograph bacteriophages on bacteria (Fig. 26).

The ability to resolve two points separately *(point resolution)* must be distinguished from the resolution of small steps *(step resolution)*. As the emission of SE is increased at sharp edges, differences of height smaller than the diameter of the primary beam can still be recognized. The differences appear as lines whose widths correspond at least to the primary beam diameter, which, of course, makes it impossible to measure them in this case (K. SCHUR et al. 1968).

Präparationsmethoden

Einführung

Eine für alle Objekte gleichermaßen geeignete Präparationsmethode kann nicht angegeben werden. Präparationsart und -dauer richten sich ganz erheblich nach Art und Größe des Objektes und nicht zuletzt nach der wissenschaftlichen Fragestellung. Ohne sich auf ein starres Präparationsschema festzulegen, sollen hier die wesentlichen Grundzüge der Objektpräparation zur rasterelektronenmikroskopischen Untersuchung dargestellt werden, die sich zum Teil an die aus der Durchstrahlungselektronenmikroskopie bekannten Verfahren anlehnen.

Da im REM das Objekt selbst und nicht wie bei der Replikatechnik ein Abdruck untersucht wird, müssen die Objekte

a) den Elektronenbeschuß aushalten können,
b) hochvakuumbeständig sein.

Sind diese beiden Forderungen erfüllt, z. B. bei Metallproben, so sind keine besonderen Präparationsschritte notwendig. Das Objekt kann sofort ins Hochvakuum eingeschleust und untersucht werden. Erfüllt das Objekt die beiden obengenannten Bedingungen nicht von vornherein, so sind zunächst weitere Präparationsschritte erforderlich. Auch in diesen Fällen ist jedoch die erforderliche Präparation für die rasterelektronenmikroskopische Untersuchung meist leichter als für die Durchstrahlungselektronenmikroskopie.

Wie im Abschnitt über die Sekundärelektronenemission gezeigt wurde, treten bei isolierenden Proben, aber auch schon bei Probenauflagerungen ohne leitende Verbindung zum Probenuntergrund, *Aufladungserscheinungen* auf. Diese stören die Abbildung und können sie unmöglich machen. Ein Beispiel für Bildstörungen durch mäßige Aufladung zeigt Abb. 27a und b. Hier liegt eine schlecht leitende Faser lose auf einem regelmäßigen Ag-Gitter. Durch die Aufladung der Faser entstehen unerwünschte Hell-Dunkel-Zeichnungen, Verzerrungen bei der Abbildung des Gitters unter der Faser sowie Versetzungen des ganzen Bildes, wenn

Techniques of Specimen Preparation

Introduction

No single method of specimen preparation is equally suitable for all types of specimen. The technique and time taken for preparation depend very much on the type and size of the specimen and not least on the purpose of the investigation. The following description lists the specimen preparation methods used for scanning electron microscopy. Some of them are similar to those used in transmission electron microscopy.

Since the specimen itself, and not a replica, is being examined, it must be able to withstand:

a) electron bombardment,
b) high vacuum.

When, as in metal specimens, both these conditions are met, no further special preparation is required. The specimen can be inserted immediately into the high vacuum system and examined. Even if the specimen does not fulfil the two abovementioned requirements, preparation for SEM examination is often easier than that required for transmission electron microscopy.

As explained in the section on the emission of secondary electrons, *charging phenomena* occur in insulating specimens, and also if the specimen has a coating which is not well grounded. They disturb or completely prevent the formation of a picture. An example of disturbances caused by moderately slight charging can be seen in Fig. 27a und b, where a fiber of low conductivity is lying on, but is not attached to, an Ag grid. The charging of the fiber causes undesired light-dark markings, distortions in the imaging of the lattice below the fiber, and also, if the charge jumps during the exposure, displacements of the whole picture. Further

a

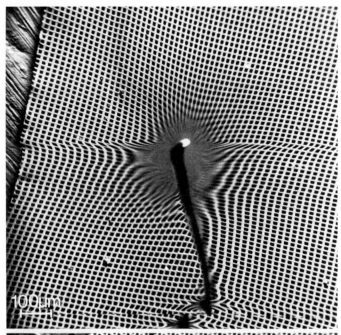

b

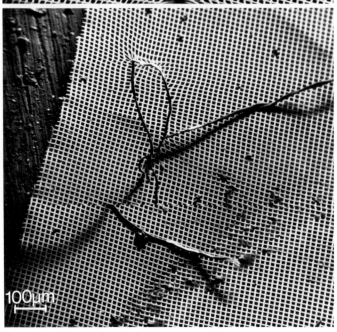

Abb. 27 a und b Typische *Aufladungserscheinungen:* Ungewöhnliche Hell-Dunkel-Zeichnungen, Bildverzerrungen, Versetzungen, demonstriert an Fäden auf einem Ag-Gitter.

Fig. 27 a and b Typical *charging phenomena:* Unusual light-dark markings, picture distortions, displacements. Threads on an Ag grid.

sich die Aufladung während der Aufnahme sprunghaft ändert. Weitere Beispiele für die manchmal verheerenden Auswirkungen von Aufladungen geben Abb. 37 und 38 wieder. Deshalb ist die Vermeidung von Aufladungen ein sehr wichtiges Ziel bei der Präparation der Objekte für rasterelektronenmikroskopische Untersuchungen.

Die *Elektronenbelastung* des Objektes ergibt sich nach Pease u. Mitarb. (1966) aus folgender Abschätzung: Geht man von einem Primärstrahlstrom von 10^{-11} A und einer Primärstrahlspannung von 20 kV aus, so beträgt die Reichweite der Elektronen in Kohlenwasserstoffen etwa 10^{-3} cm. Wird nun weiter vereinfachend angenommen, daß die Energie gleichmäßig in einem halbkugelförmigen Bereich mit dem Radius von 10^{-3} cm in Wärme umgesetzt wird, so kommt man auf eine Belastung des Objektes von etwa 100 W cm^{-3}. Diese Belastung ist wesentlich geringer als die im Durchstrahlungselektronenmikroskop, zumal infolge des Rasterverfahrens der Elektronenstrahl nur kurz auf einem Punkt verweilt. Dennoch werden auch im REM an empfindlichen Objekten Beschädigungen durch den Elektronenstrahl beobachtet.

Ein wesentlich schwierigeres Problem ist gerade im biologisch-medizinischen Bereich der hohe *Wassergehalt* vieler Proben, der mit der Forderung nach Vakuumbeständigkeit des Objektes kollidiert. Eine gewebeschonende, möglichst artefaktfreie Entwässerung der biologischen Präparate ist daher für diese Untersuchung im Hochvakuum erforderlich.

Weiterhin muß es das Ziel jeder Präparationstechnik sein, eine möglichst *artefaktfreie Oberfläche* zu gewinnen und darüber hinaus gegebenenfalls eine *Materialdifferenzierung* dieser Oberfläche zu ermöglichen. Um alle diese Forderungen zu erfüllen, wurde in enger Anlehnung an die Durchstrahlungselektronenmikroskopie (vgl. Reimer [1967], Schimmel [1969] u. a.) eine Reihe von Präparationsverfahren ausgearbeitet, von denen hier nur die wichtigsten angeführt werden sollen. Je nach Aufgabenstellung ergibt sich auf dem Gebiet der Präparationsmethoden ein reiches Experimentierfeld. Zuweilen ist

examples of the sometimes catastrophic effects of charging are given in Fig. 37 and 38. The prevention of charging is therefore a very important aim in the preparation of objects for scanning electron microscopy.

According to Pease et al. (1966), the *stress* developed in the specimen *by the primary electron beam* can be estimated as follows: If one assumes a beam current of 10^{-11} A at an accelerating voltage of 20 kV, the electron penetration in hydrocarbons is approximately 10^{-3} cm. If we take the simple case and assume that the energy is uniformly dissipated as heat in a hemispherically shaped region of radius 10^{-3} cm, the stress developed will be approximately 100 W cm^{-3}. This is considerably lower than that developed in the TEM, particularly in view of the fact that, in the scanning technique, the beam impinges on a given point of the specimen for a short time only. Beam damage can still occur, however, when very sensitive specimens are examined in the SEM.

A much more difficult problem, particularly in biological and medical fields, is the high *water content* of many specimens, which conflicts with the requirement that the specimen must withstand a high vacuum. Dehydration of biological specimens, with the tissue protected and kept free from artifacts, is therefore required for examination in high vacuum.

It should be the aim of any preparation technique to permit optimum image formation of an *artifact-free surface* and, if required, to permit *analysis and atomic number contrast*. In order to fulfil all of these demands, a number of techniques has been developed corresponding closely to those used in transmission electron microscopy (cp. Reimer [1967], Schimmel [1969] and others). Only the most important techniques will be mentioned here. Depending upon the particular requirement, methods of preparation offer ample opportunities for experimentation. At

auch bei der Rasterelektronenmikroskopie eine artefaktfreie Probenpräparation nicht möglich. Der Nachweis von Artefakten wird durch Ausführung zweier unabhängiger, verschiedener Präparationsverfahren wesentlich erleichtert.

times it is impossible to obtain a specimen free from artifacts. The existence of artifacts may be proved by using two different and independent methods of preparation.

Standardpräparation

Standard Preparation

Als erste Präparationsmaßnahme für rasterelektronenmikroskopische Untersuchungen ist häufig ein *Zerkleinern des Objektes* bis auf etwa Bohnengröße notwendig. Das Objekt wird dann mit einer geeigneten Klemmvorrichtung oder einem vakuumfesten Kleber auf den *Objektteller montiert* und *mit Leitsilber gut geerdet.* Da der Objektteller wenig Rückstreuelektronen liefern soll, werden solche aus Al oder C bevorzugt. Eine *rauhe Oberfläche des Objekttellers verbessert die Haftung von Objekt bzw. Kleber.* Das Präparat ist mit dem Objektteller so zu orientieren, daß mit den Kipp- und Drehmöglichkeiten der Probenbühne alle gewünschten Betrachtungsrichtungen eingestellt werden können.

Der Sauberkeit der zu untersuchenden Oberfläche muß besondere Aufmerksamkeit geschenkt werden; andererseits ist die Gefahr der Artefaktbildung bei diesem Präparationsschritt besonders groß. Man sollte deshalb stets versuchen, mit möglichst einfachen Mitteln auszukommen. Dazu gehören z. B. das *Abblasen von Staub* mit Frigen aus einer Sprühdose oder das *Abspülen* mit geeigneten Flüssigkeiten. Der Spüleffekt läßt sich durch vorsichtiges Pinseln bis Bürsten der Objektoberfläche verstärken, wenn das Präparat dies zuläßt. Festsitzende Beläge auf Metallproben lassen sich häufig in einem *Ultraschallbad* entfernen. Öl- und Fettfilme verschmieren häufig die Oberfläche. Einmaliges Waschen in einem Lösungsmittel genügt dann meist nicht. Deshalb sollten poröse, fetthaltige Proben (z. B. Knochen) sehr sorgfältig *entfettet* werden. Schleim- und Gewebereste können mit *Fermentbehandlung* entfernt werden; dies kann jedoch einen massiven Eingriff in die Gewebestruktur mit entsprechender großer Artefaktgefahr darstellen.

The first preparatory step for SEM investigations is to *break down the object* to about the size of a bean. The object is then *mounted on the specimen stub* with a suitable clamping device or vacuum-resistant adhesive and *carefully grounded with conductive silver.* As the stub should produce few backscattered electrons, it is preferably made of Al or C. The *adhesion of the object is improved if the stub has a rough surface.* The object with its support should be so orientated that the tilting and rotation facilities of the stage are sufficient to enable the specimen to be examined from any desired direction.

Particular attention must be paid to the cleanliness of the surface to be investigated. There will otherwise be a big risk of artifact formation at this stage of the preparation procedure. One should therefore try at all times to manage with the simplest cleaning techniques. These include *removing dust* with Frigen propellent gas from a spray can and *rinsing* with suitable liquids. The rinsing effect can be reinforced by careful brushing if the specimen will tolerate this treatment. Firm deposits on metal specimens can often be removed in an *ultrasonic bath.* Frequently there is a film of oil or grease on the surface which cannot be removed simply by *washing with a solvent.* Porous specimens containing grease (e.g., bones) should therefore be *degreased* with great care. Slime and tissue residues can be removed by *enzyme treatment,* but this may have a drastic effect on the structure of the tissue, with a correspondingly high risk of artifact formation.

Als nächster Präparationsschritt folgt dann die *Beschichtung des Präparates mit einem elektronenleitfähigen Überzug,* meist eine Bedampfung mit C und Au (Kohlenstoff-Gold-Bedampfung). Als Richtwert für diese Kohle-Schwermetall-Schicht kann eine Dicke von 30–50 nm angesehen werden. Man kann jedoch ohne weiteres bei niedrigen Vergrößerungen zu wesentlich dickeren Bedampfungsschichten übergehen, wenn eine Kegelbedampfung erfolgt. Bei sauberer Bedampfung werden im allgemeinen nur die feinsten, im REM nicht sichtbaren Oberflächenstrukturen eingeebnet (snowing-effect). Mit dieser Kohle-Schwermetall-Bedampfung werden verschiedene Zwecke erreicht:

a) Das Präparat wird mit einem gut haftenden leitfähigen Überzug versehen, wobei die C-Bedampfung als Vorbekernung für die Schwermetallbedampfung dient. Die leichten C-Atome gelangen durch Zusammenstöße mit Restgasatomen auch an Objektstellen, die im geometrischen Schatten liegen. Außerdem ist der Kohlefilm meist elastisch genug, um auch bei mehrmaligem Belüften und Evakuieren des Präparates nicht zu reißen. Damit ist eine elektrostatische Aufladung nichtleitender Proben, die zu einem den Oberflächenkontrast störenden Potentialkontrast führt, weitgehend unmöglich gemacht.

b) Durch den Schwermetallüberzug werden eine hohe Sekundärelektronenausbeute und ein gutes Auflösungsvermögen erzielt. Deshalb werden manchmal auch Proben bedampft, die selbst bereits eine elektronenleitfähige Oberfläche besitzen.

c) Die Eindringtiefe der Elektronen wird herabgesetzt und eine bessere Wärmeableitung ermöglicht, was wiederum eine Schonung des Präparates bedeutet.

Außer durch Bedampfen lassen sich leitfähige Metallschichten auch durch *Kathodenzerstäubung* aufbringen. Entsprechende Geräte werden von mehreren Firmen angeboten (z. B. Abb. 28a und b). Derartige Schichten weisen manchmal höhere SE-Emissionskoeffizienten auf als Aufdampfschichten. Bei der Kathodenzerstäubung erreichen die Metallatome das Objekt mit höherer Energie als beim Aufdampfen und haften deshalb fester an der Oberfläche; da Platzwechselvorgänge unterblei-

The next step is to *provide the specimen with an electron-conductive coating,* generally a vapor coating of carbon and gold. A suitable thickness for this carbon/heavy metal layer is approximately 30–50 nm. It is, however, possible to use much thicker coatings for low magnifications. When a proper cone shadowing evaporation technique is used, only slight snowing effects are observed. This coating serves several purposes:

a) The specimen is furnished with an adherent conductive coat. The light C atoms colliding with residual gas atoms are also deposited on areas of the specimen which lie in geometric shadows. The carbon film is also sufficiently elastic not to tear, even if the specimen is exposed several times to air and renewed vacuum. The coating prevents the build-up of an electrostatic charge on insulating regions of the specimen, which would lead to potential contrast and hence interfere with the contrast of the imaged surface obtained.

b) Heavy metal coating gives a high emission rate of secondary electrons and good resolution. For this reason even conductive specimens are sometimes coated.

c) The electron penetration is reduced and heat conducted away more efficiently, which results in better specimen preservation.

Conductive metal coats can also be applied by *sputtering.* Suitable sputtering apparatuses, such as the one shown in Fig. 28 a and b are made by several companies. The resulting coats have higher SE emission coefficients than vapor coats in some cases. As compared with the atoms of vapor coats, the metal atoms of sputter coats contain more energy on reaching the object and therefore adhere more firmly. Pre-evaporation with C is unnecessary be-

a

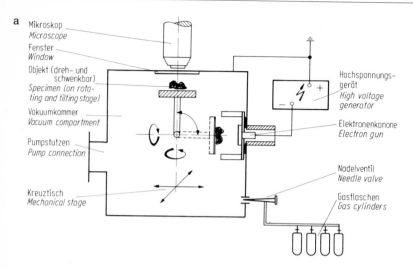

Mikroskop
Microscope

Fenster
Window

Objekt (dreh- und
schwenkbar)
*Specimen (on rota-
ting and tilting stage)*

Vakuumkammer
Vacuum compartment

Pumpstutzen
Pump connection

Kreuztisch
Mechanical stage

Hochspannungs-
gerät
*High voltage
generator*

Elektronenkanone
Electron gun

Nadelventil
Needle valve

Gasflaschen
Gas cylinders

b

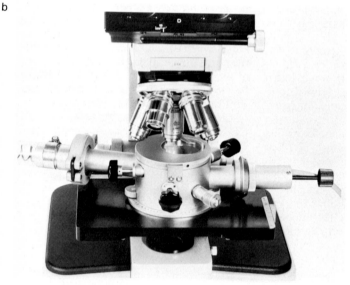

Abb. 28. *Kammer zur Metallbeschichtung* durch Kathodenzerstäubung.
a) Blockschaltbild Metallbeschichtungskammer.
b) Außenansicht einer Metallbeschichtungskammer in Kombination mit einem Lichtmikroskop.
(E. Leitz GmbH, Wetzlar)

Fig. 28. *Gas ion reaction chamber for metal coating* by sputtering.
a) Block diagram.
b) Outside view of gas ion reaction chamber used in conjunction
with a light microscope.

ben, kann auf eine Vorbekernung mit C verzichtet werden. Die Temperaturbelastung des Objektes ist ebenfalls gering, da es keine heiße Verdampfungsquelle gibt. Steht weniger die Abbildung der Oberfläche als vielmehr die *Materialdifferenzierung und Oberflächenanalyse* im Vordergrund, so muß man auf die Schwermetall-Bedampfung verzichten. In diesem Fall ist auch ein *Besprühen mit einem Antistatikum* möglich. Das Antistatikum muß jedoch ohne das Zutreten von Luftfeuchtigkeit wirksam werden können. Für rasterelektronenmikroskopische Präparationen hat sich Duron*-Spray bewährt (SIKORSKI u. SPRENKMANN 1968). Der Verwendung von Antistatikum zur Schnellpräparation anstelle einer Kohle-Schwermetall-Bedampfung stehen jedoch bei medizinischen und biologischen Objekten erhebliche Bedenken entgegen, da eine Schädigung der Zellwände eintreten kann (HERBST u. MULTIER 1969).

Mit der Standardpräparation und ihren Variationen können Metalle, Kunststoffe und andere Hartgewebe ohne weiteres untersucht werden. Bei Weichgeweben, wie sie in Medizin und Biologie überwiegend vorliegen, muß vor der Kohle-Schwermetall-Bedampfung zunächst eine *Fixierung* und *Trocknung des Präparates* vorgenommen werden, um ein vakuumbeständiges Objekt zu erhalten.

cause surface migration of gold atoms does not occur. In addition, as the source of the atoms is not hot, the object is not exposed to severe conditions of temperature.

If the image of the surface is less important than atomic number contrast and analysis of the surface, one can also *spray with antistatics*. The antistatic must, however, be effective without the introduction of moisture. For SEM specimens the Duron* spray has proved its worth (SIKORSKI and SPRENKMANN 1968). The use of antistatics for rapid preparation, instead of carbon/heavy metal coating, is open to considerable objections since cell walls may be damaged (HERBST and MULTIER 1969).

With this standard preparation and its variations, metals, plastics and other hard materials can be examined. Soft materials, which predominate in medicine and biology, have to undergo *fixation* and *drying* before being submitted to carbon or heavy metal coating in order to withstand the vacuum.

Fixation und Trocknung

Eine *einfache Trocknung des Objektes* kann zu starken Veränderungen der dreidimensionalen Oberflächenstruktur infolge der Oberflächenspannung an der Phasengrenze zwischen Flüssigkeit und Gas führen. Am stärksten tritt dies bei wasserhaltigen Objekten auf. Deshalb bietet sich ein *Trocknen aus Flüssigkeiten mit geringerer Oberflächenspannung (Alkohol, Azeton) als Wasser* an. Durch die gewählte Flüssigkeit wird das in der Probe enthaltene Wasser schrittweise ersetzt. Um die Oberflächenspannung völlig auszuschalten, empfiehlt sich die *Trocknung am kritischen Punkt.*

Fixation and Drying

Merely drying the object may lead to big changes in the three-dimensional surface structure as a result of the surface tension at the interface between liquid and gas. Water has an especially high surface tension. *Drying from liquids whose surface tension is lower than that of water, e.g., alcohol and acetone,* is therefore an obvious possibility. The water present in the specimen is gradually replaced by the chosen liquid. To eliminate the surface tension completely, it is advisable to *dry at the critical point.* This can now be done without diffi-

---

* Bezugsquelle: Hansawerke D-2800 Bremen-Hemelingen

---

* Supplied by Hansawerke D-2800 Bremen-Hemelingen

Sie ist heute ohne großen Aufwand mit kommerziellen Geräten durchführbar (Abb. 29). Im Zustandsdiagramm (Abb. 30) wird von Punkt A ausgehend der Weg 2 durchlaufen. Man umgeht den kritischen Punkt (CP = critical point), bei dem die Phasengrenze flüssig/gasförmig endet, durch Erhöhen der Temperatur und des Druckes. Da danach keine Oberflächenspannungen mehr wirksam sind, kann man durch vorsichtige Abnahme des Druckes und der Temperatur den Trocknungspunkt B ohne Zellschädigung erreichen. Der kritische Punkt von H_2O (kritischer Druck P_k = 220 bar, kritische Temperatur T_k = 374 °C) liegt für die Probenpräparation biologischer Objekte ungünstig. Man verwendet daher besser CO_2 (P_k = 74 bar, T_k = 31 °C) oder Freon 13 (P_k = 40 bar, T_k = 39 °C). Im letzten Fall wird dem Objekt zunächst in einer aufsteigenden Alkoholreihe das Wasser entzogen; der Alkohol wird dann erst gegen Freon 11 und dieses wiederum gegen Freon 13 ausgetauscht. Nun kann nun die beschriebene Trocknung jenseits des kritischen Punktes durchgeführt werden. Anhand von Untersuchungen empfindlicher Insektenaugen (FROMME u. Mitarb. 1972) lassen sich Trocknungsartefakte und ihre Vermeidung besonders gut demonstrieren. Während bei Culex pipiens die kutikuläre Cornea stets Faltungen aufweist, bleibt ihre anatomische Struktur nach Trocknung am kritischen Punkt erhalten (Abb. 31a und b). Bei Abb. 32a und b (Augen von Tipula oleracea) glaubt man wegen der regelmäßig gestalteten Einsenkung in hexagonale Becher zunächst nicht an ein Trocknungsartefakt, das dennoch vorliegt, wie Abb. 32b des gleichen Objektes nach Trocknung am kritischen Punkt beweist. Allerdings scheint hier die kritische Punkttrocknung allein noch nicht für eine völlig artefaktfreie Abbildung auszureichen, es sind noch Faltenabbildungen sichtbar. Diese lassen sich durch geeignete Fixation vermeiden.

Flüssigkeitshaltige Objekte können durch Einfrieren in den festen Aggregatzustand überführt werden (Weg 1 in Abb. 30). Um Veränderungen an der Objektoberfläche durch Bildung großer Kristalle bei langsamer Abkühlung zu vermeiden, benutzt

culty with the help of commercial apparatuses (Fig. 29). In the phase diagram (Fig. 30), one starts at point A and follows path 2. The critical point (CP) at which the liquid/gaseous interface ends is overcome by raising the temperature and pressure. As no surface tensions are active thereafter, point B can be reached, without damage to the cells, by slowly reducing the pressure and temperature. The critical point of H_2O (critical pressure P_k = 220 bar; critical temperature T_k = 374 °C) is unfavorable to the preparation of biological specimens. It is therefore preferable to use CO_2 (P_k = 74 bar; T_k = 31 °C) or Freon 13 (P_k = 40 bar; T_k = 39 °C). In the latter case, the water is first removed from the object in ascending alcohol concentrations; the alcohol is then exchanged for Freon 11, which, in turn, is exchanged for Freon 13. The drying procedure described can then be carried out above the critical point.

Tests performed on sensitive insect eyes (FROMME et al. 1972) illustrate particularly well the formation of artifacts and how they can be avoided. After air drying the cuticular cornea of Culex pipiens always displays folds, but its anatomical structure is retained if critical point drying is applied (Fig. 31 a, b). Because of the regularity of the hexagonal depressions, a drying artifact is not immediately suspected in Fig. 32 a and b (eyes of Tipula oleracea). A photograph of the same object after drying at the critical point (Fig. 32b) proves, however, that such an artifact is present. Nevertheless, it appears that in this case drying at the critical point is not by itself sufficient to eliminate artifacts entirely, as folds are still visible. Their formation can be prevented by suitable fixation.

Objects containing liquids can be solidified by freezing (path 1 in Fig. 30). Changes to the surface through the formation of large ice crystals in the process of slow

Abb. 29. Gerät zur Trock-
nung am kritischen Punkt
(für Frigen). (Bomar,
SPC-900, Cambridge
Instrument Comp.,
Dortmund)

Fig. 29. Device for drying
at the critical point
(suitable for Frigen).

Abb. 30. *Gefriertrocknung*
(Weg 1) und *Trocknung
am kritischen Punkt*
(Weg 2) von A nach B in
einem schematischen Zu-
standsdiagramm.

Fig. 30. *Freeze-drying*
(path 1) and *drying at the
critical point* (path 2) from
A to B in a schematic
phase diagram.

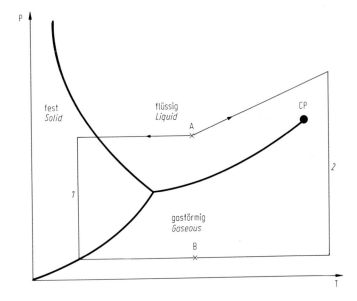

a

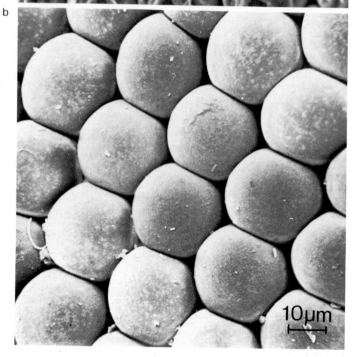

b

Abb. 31. Augen einer Stechmücke (Culex pipiens) in Abhängigkeit von der Präparation.
a) Nach Lufttrocknung,
b) nach Trocknung am kritischen Punkt.
(H. G. Fromme, M. Pfautsch, G. Pfefferkorn, F. Bystricky, 1972)

Fig. 31. Eyes of a mosquito (Culex pipiens).
a) After air drying,
b) After drying at the critical point.

Abb. 32. Auge der Kohl-
schnake (Tipula oleracea)
in Abhängigkeit von der
Präparation.
a) Nach Lufttrocknung,
b) nach Trocknung am
   kritischen Punkt.
(*H. G. Fromme,
M. Pfautsch, G. Pfef-
ferkorn, F. Bystricky,*
1972)

Fig. 32. Eye of a cranefly
(Tipula oleracea).
a) After air drying,
b) After drying at the
   critical point.

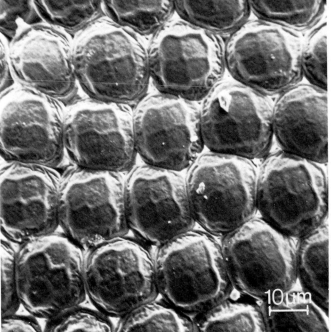

33 a

man den plötzlichen *Gefrierschock*. Man kann z. B. das Objekt in flüssigen Stickstoff am Gefrierpunkt eintauchen; in diesem Fall tritt das den Wärmeübergang behindernde Leidenfrostsche Phänomen nicht auf. Die gefrorenen Objekte können auf einem Kühltisch (z. B. mittels Kühlkette nach FUCHS u. LINDEMANN [1975]) direkt in das REM gebracht werden (Abb. 33). Dies empfiehlt sich vor allem für mikroanalytische Untersuchungen leicht beweglicher Ionen (Na⁺, K⁺).

Um alle weiteren Präparationen und Untersuchungen bei Zimmertemperatur durchführen zu können, kann man auch das Objekt im Hochvakuum im tiefgekühlten Zustand trocknen (*Gefriertrocknung*). Der Aufwand ist hier gegenüber der Trocknung am kritischen Punkt größer, besonders wenn, wie im REM üblich, relativ große Proben zu untersuchen sind. Da beide Trocknungsverfahren völlig unabhängig voneinander sind, können beide nebeneinander als Kontrollversuche zur Erkennung von Artefakten durchgeführt werden.

cooling can be avoided by *shock freezing*. For example, the object can be immersed in liquid nitrogen at this liquid's freezing point; in this case Leidenfrost's phenomenon, which impedes the transfer of heat, does not occur. The frozen objects can be introduced into the SEM directly on a refrigerated table (by means of a refrigeration chain according to FUCHS and LINDEMANN [1975]; e.g., Fig. 33). This is particularly recommended for microanalytical investigations of mobile ions (Na⁺, K⁺).

In order that further preparation steps and investigations can be carried out at room temperature, the object can also be dried in a high vacuum in the deep-frozen state *(freeze-drying)*. This is a more costly and time-consuming procedure than drying at the critical point, especially when relatively large specimens are needed, as they usually are for the SEM. As the two drying procedures are completely independent of one another, they can be used side by side to check each other in respect of the formation of artifacts.

33 b

Abb. 33. Kühlkette nach *Fuchs* und *Lindemann:*
a) Mit Hilfe einer evakuierbaren Schleuse (links) kann das Objekt aus einer Präparationsanlage (z. B. EPA 100, Abb. 35) auf den Kühltisch (rechts) im REM ohne Unterbrechung des Vakuums gebracht werden.
b) Schleuse, angeflanscht an ein Stereoscan.
(Cambridge Instrument Comp., Dortmund)

Fig. 33. Refrigeration chain according to *Fuchs* and *Lindemann:*
a) By means of an evacuable airlock (left) the specimen can be transferred from a preparation apparatus (e.g., EPA 100, Fig. 35) to the refrigerated table of the SEM (right) without interrupting the vacuum.
b) Airlock attached to a Stereoscan.

Besteht die Gefahr, daß das getrocknete Objekt kollabiert, oder sind beim Flüssigkeitsaustausch Schrumpfungen bzw. Quellungen zu erwarten, so muß das Material vorher *fixiert* werden. Unter den verschiedenen, für die elektronenmikroskopische Präparation von Zellen und Geweben gebräuchlichen Fixiermittel kommen Osmiumtetroxid (OsO_4), Aldehyden und Permanganationen besondere Bedeutung zu.

Als wichtigster Reaktionsmechanismus bei der *OsO_4-Fixierung* wird die Ausbildung von Estern an den Doppelbindungen ungesättigter Fettsäuren angesehen. Das Osmium wird dabei reduziert, das organische Material oxidiert. Wahrscheinlich ist darüber hinaus mit einer Polykondensation, vor allem von Lipoiden zu rechnen. Die *Fixierwirkung von $KMnO_4$,* vor allem bei pflanzlichen Geweben eingesetzt, dürfte ähnlich verlaufen wie die von OsO_4. *Aldehyde* wirken vernetzend auf die Proteine der Zellen. Glutaraldehyd (OHC–[CH$_2$]$_3$ – CHO) wird wegen des Vorhandenseins zweier funktioneller Gruppen meist gegenüber Formaldehyd bevorzugt.

Im Gegensatz zu den meisten lichtmikroskopischen Fixiermitteln werden in der Elektronenmikroskopie die Fixiermittel meist nur in Verbindung mit Zusätzen, die den pH-Wert und die Osmolarität des Mediums auf physiologische Werte bringen, verwendet. Prinzipiell ist die *Isotonie der Fixierungslösung* mit dem Gewebe anzustreben. Die richtige Einstellung des pH-Wertes erfolgt durch Pufferlösungen (z. B. Veronal-Azetat-Puffer nach Michaelis, Phosphatpuffer nach Millonig, Rezepte bei REIMER [1967] und SCHIMMEL [1969]). Diese Einstellung ist bei tierischen Geweben kritischer als bei pflanzlichen, da bei letzteren die pH-Werte häufig bereits im sauren Bereich liegen und der Zusatz von Aldehyden oder OsO_4-Lösungen keine großen Änderungen hervorruft. Zur Tonizitätssteigerung wird der Pufferlösung manchmal Saccharose oder Glucose zugegeben.

Abschließend seien die *Rezepte für zwei häufig verwendete Fixierlösungen* angegeben (nach PLATTNER in SCHIMMEL 1969):

If there is a risk that the dried object will collapse or if the exchange of liquids is expected to cause shrinkage or swelling, the material must be fixed. Among the various fixatives used to prepare cells and tissues for electron microscopy, osmium tetroxide (OsO_4), aldehydes and permanganate ions are particularly important. In *fixation with OsO_4* the most important reaction mechanism is considered to be the formation of esters on the double bonds of unsaturated fatty acids. Here the osmium is reduced and the organic matter oxidized. In addition, polycondensation – especially of lipoids – probably occurs also. The *fixative action of $KMnO_4$,* particularly on plant tissues, is probably similar to that of OsO_4. *Aldehydes* cross-link the proteins of the cells. Glutaraldehyde (OHC-(CH$_2$)$_3$-CHO) is usually preferred to formaldehyde owing to the presence of two functional groups.

Unlike most fixatives used for light microscopy, those used for electron microscopy are generally used only in conjunction with additives which adjust the pH value and osmolar concentration of the medium to physiological levels. In principle, *isotonicity of the fixative solution* with the tissue is desirable. Correct adjustment of the pH value can be achieved with buffer solutions (e.g., barbital acetate buffer according to Michaelis; phosphate buffer according to Millonig; contents given by REIMER [1967] and SCHIMMEL [1969]). This adjustment is more critical with animal tissues than with vegetable ones because the pH values of the latter are often in the acid range already and addition of aldehydes or OsO_4 solutions causes no important changes. Sucrose or glucose is sometimes added to the buffer solution to raise the tonicity.

The contents for two frequently used fixative solutions (from PLATTNER in SCHIMMEL 1969) are as follows:

1. *OsO₄-Fixans für Säugetiergewebe*
Stammlösungen:

a) $NaH_2PO_4 \cdot H_2O$, 2,26%ig in Aqua dest. (für Puffer),
b) NaOH, 2,52%ig in Aqua dest. (für Einstellung des pH-Wertes),
c) Glucose, 5,4%ig, in Aqua dest. (für Plasmaisotonie),
d) Mischlösung aus 41,5 ml Lösung a und 8,5 ml Lösung b.

Zur Herstellung der Fixierlösung mische man 45 ml Lösung d mit 5 ml Lösung c und gebe 0,5 g OsO_4 (Trockensubstanz) zu. Es stellt sich ein pH-Wert von 7,3 bis 7,4 ein; andere Werte können durch Variation der Menge von Lösung b erreicht werden.
Achtung: Der Anfänger sei eindringlich auf die Vergiftungsgefahren bei Arbeiten mit OsO_4 (Dampfdruck 17 mb bei Raumtemperatur, MAK-Wert 0,002 mg/m³) hingewiesen; die Sicherheitsvorschriften (Schutzhandschuhe, Schutzbrille, Abzug) sind unbedingt genau einzuhalten!

2. *Aldehyd-Fixans für nicht besonders empfindliche Gewebe*
Stammlösungen:

a) 0,1 M Na_2HPO_4 (= 7,1 g Na_2HPO_4 wasserfrei in 500 ml Aqua dest.),
b) 0,1 M KH_2PO_4 (= 6,8 g KH_2PO_4 in 500 ml Aqua dest.),
c) 7–8 Teile Lösung a + 2 bis 3 Teile Lösung b ergeben einen 0,1 M Phosphatpuffer mit pH = 7,2-7,4,
d) 25%iger Glutaraldehyd (frisch vorgereinigt).
Fixierlösung: 2 Teile c + 1 Teil d + 1 Teil Aqua dest. Zum Auswaschen des überschüssigen Fixiermittels werden 6,85 g Sacharose in 100 ml Phosphatpuffer gelöst.

Das Zusammenwirken und die *Reihenfolge der wichtigsten Präparationsschritte für biologische Objekte* ist in Abb. 34 schematisch dargestellt. Ein vielseitiges Präparationsgerät, mit dem Trocknung, Gefriertrocknung und Bedampfung durchgeführt werden können, ist z. B. die Anlage EPA 100 der Firma Leybold-Hereaeus, Köln (Abb. 35).

1. *OsO₄ fixative for mammal tissues*
Stock solutions:

a) $NaH_2PO_4 \cdot H_2O$, 2.26% in aqua dest. (for buffer)
b) NaOH, 2.52% in aqua dest. (for adjustment of the pH value)
c) Glucose, 5.4% in aqua dest. (for plasma isotonicity)
d) Mixture of solutions a and b in the ratio 41.5 : 8.5 ml.

The fixative solution is prepared by mixing 45 ml of solution d with 5 ml of solution c and adding 0.5 g of OsO_4 (dry substance). The pH value of the solution will be 7.3 to 7.4; different values can be obtained by varying the amount of solution b.
Warning: The inexperienced are warned most emphatically of the risks of poisoning which arise during work with OsO_4 (vapor pressure 17 mb at room temperature, maximum allowable workplace concentration in the Federal Republic of Germany 0.002 mg/m³). Strict compliance with the requisite safety precautions (wearing of protective gloves and goggles, use of air extractors) is essential!

2. *Aldehyde fixative for not particularly sensitive tissues*
Stock solutions:

a) 0.1 M Na_2HPO_4 (= 7.1 g dehydrated Na_2HPO_4 in 500 ml aqua dest.)
b) 0.1 M KH_2PO_4 (= 6.8 g KH_2PO_4 in 500 ml aqua dest.)
c) 7–8 parts solution a + 2 to 3 parts solution b give a 0.1 M phosphate buffer of pH 7.2-7.4
d) 25% glutaraldehyde (freshly purified).

To prepare the fixative solution, mix 2 parts of c with 1 part of d + 1 part of aqua dest. To wash out the excessive fixative, dissolve 6.85 g of sucrose in 100 ml of phosphate buffer.

The order of the *main steps in the preparation of biological specimens* and their interactions are shown schematically in Fig. 34. A multipurpose instrument for drying, freeze-drying and coating is manufactured by Leybold-Heraeus, Cologne, and is known as the EPA 100 (Fig. 35).

48

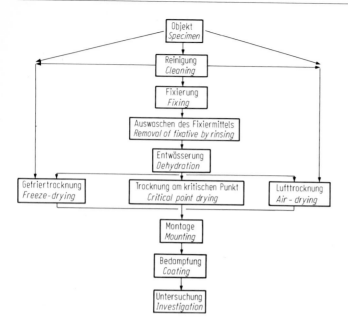

Abb. 34. Schematische Darstellung der *wichtigen Präparationsschritte in der Rasterelektronenmikroskopie.*

Fig. 34. Schematic diagram of the *main steps in the preparation of specimens for scanning electron microscopy.*

Abb. 35. Elektronenmikroskopische Präparationsanlage (EPA 100) der Firma Leybold-Heraeus, Köln.

Fig. 35. Unit for specimen preparation (EPA 100), Leybold-Heraeus, Cologne.

Spezielle Präparationsmaßnahmen

Infolge der außergewöhnlichen Schärfentiefe des REM können auch stark zerklüftete Objekte untersucht werden. Dabei ist es jedoch häufig schwierig, eine zusammenhängende leitfähige Schicht aufzubringen, was wiederum zu störenden *Aufladungseffekten* führen kann. In vielen Fällen können Aufladungen dennoch vermieden werden, wenn das Präparat vor dem Evakuieren längere Zeit in OsO_4-Dampf gestanden hat. OsO_4 wird von vielen organischen Verbindungen reduziert, so daß sich auch an Stellen, die sonst durch keine Bedampfung erreicht werden können, ein hinreichend leitfähiger Überzug bildet. Geringe Eigenbewegungen des Objektes, z. B. beim Belüften und Evakuieren oder Quellen und Schrumpfen des Objektes bei Lagerung der getrockneten Proben an der Luft, können zu *Rissen in der sehr dünnen Bedampfungsschicht* führen. Dies kann vermieden werden, indem eine Präparationskammer mit der Objektkammer des REM verbunden und die zu untersuchende Probe ohne Unterbrechung des Vakuums unter den Elektronenstrahl gebracht wird (Anbau einer elektronenmikroskopischen Präparationsanlage, z. B. EPA 100, an ein Stereoscan).

Das REM dient hauptsächlich zur Abbildung von Objektoberflächen. Will man den Anschluß an die Durchstrahlungselektronenmikroskopie gewinnen, so kann im *REM auch ein Dünnschnittpräparat* bei Elektronendurchstrahlung betrachtet (auch kleine Vergrößerungen sind damit zugänglich) oder der zum Dünnschnitt gehörende Objektanschnitt näher untersucht werden. Häufig bieten jedoch *Objektbruchflächen* bessere Einblicke in die Innenstruktur als Objektanschnitte. Um Artefakte weitgehend zu vermeiden, sollte das Objekt spröde sein. Je spröder das Objekt, desto besser läßt sich ein informationsreiches Bruchpräparat herstellen. Deshalb wird das Objekt oft zunächst in flüssigem Stickstoff gekühlt und anschließend gebrochen (*Tieftemperaturbruch*). Zwar wird heute mit dem REM bevorzugt das Objekt selbst abgebildet, dies schließt jedoch nicht die Untersuchung von Oberflächen*abdrücken* aus. Letztere Untersu-

Special Preparation Steps

Because of the exceptional depth of focus of the SEM, even deeply undulating and jagged surfaces can be examined. Often, however, it may be difficult to obtain continuous coating, which, in turn, may lead to the troublesome effect of local surface charging. In many cases *charging* can be avoided, for instance if the specimen has been kept for a long time in OsO_4 vapor before evacuation. OsO_4 is reduced by many organic compounds, so that inaccessible areas which cannot be reached by normal evaporation can be covered adequately by this technique.

Discontinuities in the very thin coating may be caused by minor spontaneous movements in the specimen, e.g., during evacuation or re-aeration, when expansion or contraction may occur or when a specimen which has been dried is stored in air. They can be avoided if a preparation chamber is linked with the specimen chamber of the SEM so that the prepared specimen can be placed under the electron beam without interrupting the vacuum. This is possible when an electron microscopical preparation attachment (e.g., EPA 100), is fitted to a Stereoscan.

The principal use of the SEM is to obtain topographical images of specimen surfaces. With modern SEMs it is also possible to image specimens in the transmission mode. *Thin sections* can therefore be examined even at low magnification, or the area from which the thin section has been taken can be examined in the scanning mode. Possible artifacts due to microtome knives have to be considered. Often, however, *fragmented surfaces* of specimens provide a better insight into the internal structure than do sections. The more brittle the material, the easier it is to obtain a specimen with few artifacts. The material is usually cooled in liquid nitrogen and subsequently fractured (*low temperature fracture*).

It is preferable to examine the specimen itself, but this does not exclude examination of *surface replicas* in the SEM, which is

chung wird dort durchgeführt, wo ein großes Objekt nicht auf Objekttellergröße zerkleinert werden kann (z. B. Korrosionsuntersuchung an Turbinenschaufel usw.). Damit entfallen jedoch die Möglichkeiten zur Materialdifferenzierung und Analyse.

Färbungs- und Kontrastierungsverfahren können im REM über Kathodolumineszenz und Röntgenanalyse (vgl. Abb. 44 bis 46) ebenfalls ausgewertet werden. Auch die Anwendung von Ätzverfahren (z. B. spezifisches Herauslösen einer Materialkomponente, enzymatischer Abbau, Glimmätzung mit O_2, Ionenätzung) zur Materialdifferenzierung oder zur Darstellung innerer Strukturen ist möglich. Die gewonnenen Objektoberflächen sollten jedoch kritisch beurteilt werden, solange der Mechanismus des Ätzvorganges nicht vollständig klar ist.

Trotz gutem Kreisen und Pendeln des Objektes während der Beschichtung läßt es sich manchmal nicht vermeiden, daß an feinen Poren und Rissen sowie an inneren Oberflächen dennoch Aufladungserscheinungen auftreten. Hier kann eine Behandlung *mit OsO_4-Dampf für eine ausreichende Leitfähigkeit sorgen,* sofern das OsO_4 von der Substanz oder von einer dünnen Belegungsschicht reduziert wird. Auch durch *Tränken mit kolloidaler Kohle* kann man poröse Objekte in den Poren und Rissen leitfähig machen; die Suspensierung muß jedoch von der Oberfläche wieder sorgfältig abgewaschen werden.

Häufig ist es nützlich, eine in bezug auf Aufladungserscheinungen schwierige Probe durch ein *kleines Loch in einer Metallfolie* (z. B. Al) zu betrachten (Abb. 36 sowie 37a und b). Auch ein zu weitgehendes Trocknen kann unnötige Aufladungsprobleme mit sich bringen. Wie Abb. 38a und b zeigt, ist eine gewisse *Restfeuchte* durchaus von Vorteil (PFEFFERKORN u. Mitarb. 1972).

undertaken when a specimen cannot be reduced to a suitable size for the specimen holder (e.g., in corrosion studies on turbine blades). Differentiation of materials by atomic number contrast is then, however, impossible.

Staining and contrast techniques may be evaluated in the SEM by cathodoluminescence and x-ray analysis (cp. Fig. 44–46). Etching processes (e.g., specific dissolution of one phase, enzymatic action, glow discharge with O_2, ion bombardment) can be used to differentiate materials or to obtain images of internal structures. One should, however, be critical in assessing the surface structures obtained as long as the etching mechanism is not definitely known.

Even when the object is carefully rotated and swung while being coated, the appearance of charging phenomena at minute pores and cracks, as well as on interior surfaces is sometimes unavoidable. In such cases treatment with *OsO_4 vapor ensures satisfactory conductivity,* provided the OsO_4 is reduced by the substance or by a thin surface layer. The pores and cracks of porous objects can also be made conductive by *impregnation with colloidal carbon,* but the suspension remaining on the surface must be carefully washed away afterwards.

In the case of charging, it is often helpful to observe the specimen through a *small hole in a metal foil* (e.g., aluminium; Fig. 36, 37a, b). Unnecessary charging difficulties may also be caused by excessive drying. As Fig. 38a and b shows, a certain *residual moisture* is definitely advantageous (PFEFFERKORN et al. 1972).

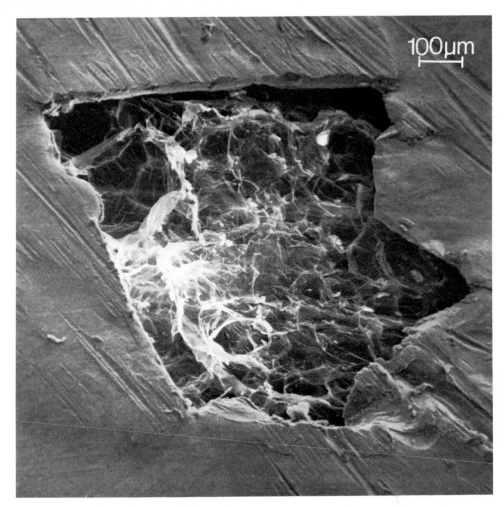

100μm

Abb. 36. *Vermeidung von Aufladungen* bei Abbildung durch ein Loch in einer Al-Folie. Objekt: Unbehandelte Kunststoffoberfläche (Styropor). (*G. E. Pfefferkorn, H. Gruter, M. Pfautsch,* 1972)

Fig. 36. Imaging through a hole in an aluminium foil to *avoid charging.* Untreated surface of a foamed plastic (Styropor).

a

b

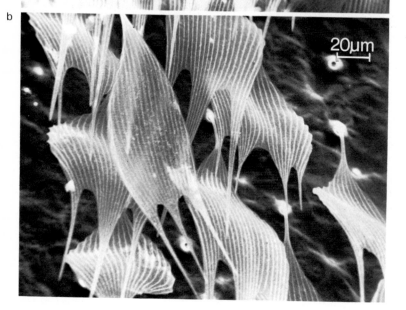

Abb. 37. *Vermeidung von Aufladungen* bei Abbildung durch ein Loch in Al-
Folie. Objekt: Schuppen eines Schmetterlingsflügels (Bombyx mori).
a) Getrocknet, unbehandelt,
b) gleiches Objekt durch ein 2-mm-Loch in Al-Folie abgebildet.
(*G. E. Pfefferkorn, H. Gruter, M. Pfautsch,* 1972)

Fig. 37. Imaging through a hole in aluminium foil to *avoid charging.* Scales of
a butterfly wing (Bombyx mori).
a) Dried, untreated
b) Same specimen imaged through a 2-mm hole in aluminium foil.

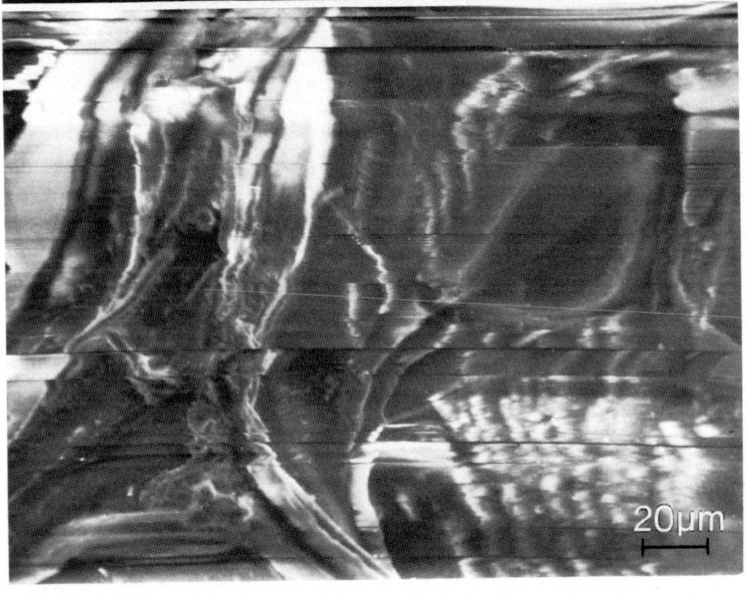

Abb. 38. Beispiel für *Aufladungen durch zu weitgehende Trocknung des Objektes.*
Objekt: Kunststoff (Styropor), unbedampft.
a) Frisch aufgeklebt, mit Leitsilber umrandet und sofort ins Rasterelektronenmikroskop eingeschleust,
b) nach 24 Stunden im Trockenschrank, abgebildet im REM.
(*G. E. Pfefferkorn, H. Gruter, M. Pfautsch,* 1972)

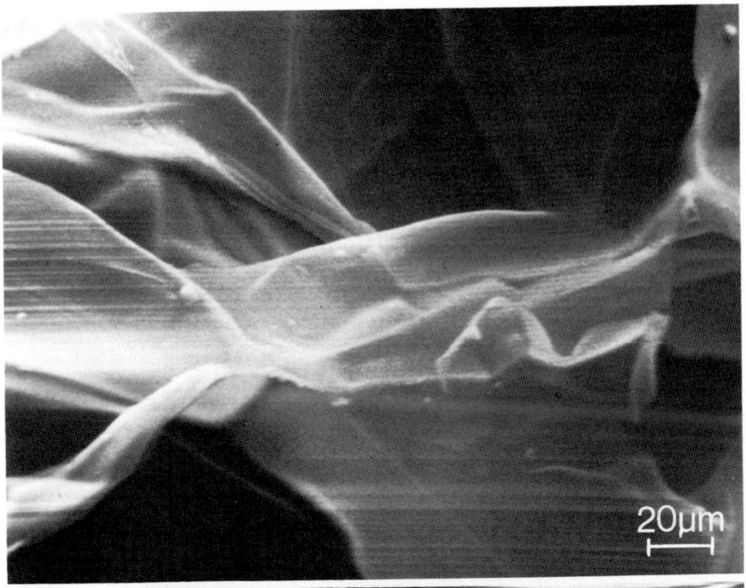

Fig. 38. Example of *charging caused by excessive drying* of the specimen.
Foamed plastic (Styropor), uncoated.
a) Freshly mounted with adhesive, surrounded with conductive silver and immediately introduced into the scanning electron microscope
b) Imaged in the SEM after 24 hours in a drying cabinet.

Nützliche Hinweise zur Aufnahmetechnik

Die Präparation ist nicht allein für eine optimale Information über die Oberfläche maßgebend; sehr viel hängt von der *Mikroskopiertechnik* ab.

Zunächst prüfe man an einem Testobjekt (z. B. Ag-Gitter), ob ein Gerät ein günstiges Signal-Rausch-Verhältnis und gutes Auflösungsvermögen bietet. Hohes Rauschen ist häufig auf schlechte Justierung der Kathode oder auf Verschleiß am Szintillator zurückzuführen. Schlechtes Auflösungsvermögen hat vielfach seine Ursachen in mangelhafter Korrektur des Astigmatismus (Abb. 39a–c). Ist eine Korrektur des Astigmatismus mit den vorgesehenen Mitteln nicht möglich, so sind gegebenenfalls die Blenden zu wechseln oder das Gerät zu putzen. Die elektronischen Hilfsmittel zur Optimierung des Kontrastes (z. B. beim Stereoscan: black-level, γ-Variation) sind voll auszuschöpfen. Wertvolle Hilfe leistet dabei ein zusätzlicher Monitor, auf den die örtliche Signalhöhe auf einer Abtastzeile durch die Y-Auslenkung dargestellt wird.

Wegen der besseren Sekundärelektronenemission und zur Verstärkung des räumlichen Eindruckes (vgl. Abb. 19) empfiehlt es sich, die zu untersuchende Objektoberfläche etwa 40 Grad gegen den Primärstrahl in Richtung des Kollektors zu neigen. Es muß jedoch dabei berücksichtigt werden, daß dann die Vergrößerung in Richtung der X- und Y-Koordinate nicht mehr genau gleich ist (Abb. 40a und b). Lineare Strukturen sind am besten zu erkennen, wenn sie parallel zur Kippachse liegen.

Ungünstige geometrische Bedingungen bei der Aufnahme lassen sich durch speziell dem Problem angepaßte Probenhalter umgehen.

Ein besseres *Auflösungsvermögen* erzielt man aus elektronenoptischen Gründen bei geringem Arbeitsabstand (breiteres Bündel). Eine größere *Schärfentiefe* erreicht man jedoch bei kleinem Aperturwinkel, der bei großem Arbeitsabstand und kleiner Aperturblende gegeben ist. Hohe Strahlstromintensität bedeutet *besseres Signal-Rausch-Verhältnis,* jedoch

Some Useful Hints for the Operator

The preparation of the specimen is not the only factor on which the information yield depends; a great deal depends also on *how the microscope is used.*

It is recommended to check daily, with the aid of a test specimen (e.g., Ag grid), whether the instrument is giving a favorable signal-to-noise ratio and good resolution. High noise levels often result from poor adjustment of the cathode or wear to the scintillator. Poor resolution is often caused by insufficient correction of astigmatism (Fig. 39a–c). If it is impossible to correct the astigmatism with the controls provided, it may be advisable to change the aperture or to clean the instrument. The electronic aids for optimization of contrast (black level and γ variation in the case of the Stereoscan) should be used to the full. Contrast optimization is greatly facilitated by an additional monitor on which the local height of the signal is represented by the Y-deflection on a scanned line.

The surface of the specimen to be examined should be tilted at 40° to the primary beam in the direction of the collector; this improves secondary electron emission and reinforces the three-dimensional impression (cp. Fig. 19). It must be remembered, however, that magnification in the direction of the X and Y coordinates alters in relation to the angle of tilt (Fig. 40a, b). Linear structures are most easily recognized when parallel to the axis of tilting. Specially adapted specimen stages may help to overcome unfavorable geometrical conditions.

For electron-optical reasons *resolution* is better with a short working distance (wider beam). *Depth of focus,* however, is improved with a small illumination aperture, i.e., a long working distance and small aperture. High beam current gives a better *signal-to-noise ratio,* but larger

Abb. 39. Ag-Gitter als *Test-objekt zur Demonstration astigmatischer Abbildungen.*
a) Normale Abbildung mit korrigiertem Astigmatis-mus.
b) und c) Beispiele für ver-schiedene Formen un-scharfer Abbildung infolge von starkem Astigmatis-mus.

Fig. 39. Ag grid as a *test object for demonstration of astigmatic images.*
a) Normal image with correc-ted astimatism
b) and c) Examples of blurring by pronounced astigmatism.

a

b

Abb. 40. *Kontamination,* erzeugt bei hoher Vergrößerung und dann bei niedriger Vergrößerung aufgenommen. Sie macht den vom Elektronenstrahl abgetasteten Bereich sichtbar.
a) Beim Neigungswinkel von 50 Grad wird der quadratische Abtastbereich zum Rechteck verzerrt,
b) mit Hilfe der *tilt correction* wird weitgehende Korrektur der Verzerrung erreicht.

Fig. 40. *Contamination* produced at high magnification and photographed at low magnification. It renders visible the area scanned by the electron beam.
a) At a tilt angle of 50° the quadratic scanned area is distorted to a rectangle.
b) The distortion is substantially eliminated by *tilt correction.*

schlechtere Bündelung und damit schlechteres Auflösungsvermögen.

Die *Betrachtung* des rasterelektronenmikroskopischen Bildes erfolgt auf einem lang nachleuchtenden Bildschirm bei relativ raschem Schreibstrahldurchlauf (etwa 1 Sekunde pro Bild). Für die *photographische* Dokumentation des rasterelektronenmikroskopischen Bildes dient eine zweite Bildröhre mit kurz nachleuchtendem Bildschirm und relativ langsamem Schreibstrahldurchlauf. Die Kamera bleibt während der gesamten Durchlaufzeit des Schreibstrahles geöffnet.

Häufig erhält man mehr Informationen aus oberflächennahen Schichten bei Verwendung niedriger Beschleunigungsspannungen (3–10 kV für dünne Membranen, s. FECHER [1971] u. a., vgl. Abb. 22 und 23). Auch die Wahl der richtigen Vergrößerung spielt eine Rolle. Sie muß so hoch sein, daß die interessierenden Details nicht im Raster des Bildes untergehen. Um diese Strukturen leicht einordnen zu können, empfiehlt es sich, zusätzlich Übersichtsaufnahmen bei geringerer Vergrößerung anzufertigen.

Manchmal stören das Bild unkontrolliert auftretende Kontaminationsquadrate. Sie rühren meist von der Wechselwirkung des Primärstrahles mit Kohlenwasserstoffmolekülen aus dem Restgas her (vgl. Abb. 22a und Abb. 40). Es ist in solchen Fällen günstig, rasch bei hoher Vergrößerung scharf zu stellen, dann aber die Aufnahmen in der Reihenfolge steigender Vergrößerung vorzunehmen.

Man kann diese Kontaminationsquadrate aber auch benutzen, um sich ein Bild von den Bilddrehungen und Verzerrungen beim Kippen bzw. Ändern des Arbeitsabstandes zu machen, sowie die elektronischen Korrekturmöglichkeiten (SCAN-Rotation, tilt-correction) zu überprüfen (Abb. 40b).

Auch an dieser Stelle sei nochmals darauf hingewiesen, daß Aufladungen mit aller Sorgfalt zu vermeiden sind. Geringere Aufladungseffekte erkennt der Ungeübte häufig nicht beim raschen Abtasten am Beobachtungsschirm; erst später wundert er sich über helle und dunkle Streifen oder über Verzerrungen im Bild (s. Abb. 27, 37 und 38).

beam diameter and therefore impaired resolution.

Examination of the SEM image is carried out on a long persistence phosphor screen with relatively rapid scan speeds (approximately 1 sec/image). A second tube with a short persistence phosphor screen and relatively slow scan speeds serves for *photographic* recording. Throughout the scan the shutter of the camera remains open.

Often the use of low accelerating voltage (3–10 kV for thin membranes, FECHER et al. [1971] among others; cp. also Fig. 22, 23) provides more information from layers near the surface of the sample.

The choice of magnification is also important. It must be high enough to ensure that the details which are of interest are not lost between the scanning lines. To facilitate the allocation of highly magnified details, it is advisable to make additional photographs at low magnification.

Sometimes the picture is disturbed by sporadically occurring contamination squares. Generally they originate from the interaction of the primary beam with hydrocarbon molecules from the residual gas (cp. Fig. 22a, 40). In such cases it is advisable to bring the specimen into focus rapidly at a high magnification, but then to take the photographs in order of increasing magnification. Contamination squares can also be used, however, to form an impression of the twisting and distortions caused by tilting or by changing the working distance and to check the facilities for electronic correction (scan rotation, tilt correction) (Fig. 40b).

It should be mentioned once more that extreme care should be taken to prevent charging. Often the novice fails to recognize charging effects when he is watching the monitor at high scan rates. Afterwards, however, he is surprised to find light and dark strips or distortions in the picture (see Fig. 27, 37, 38).

Das REM liefert zwar bei geeigneter Anordnung von Primärstrahl, Probe und Kollektor infolge der außergewöhnlichen Schärfentiefe bisher unerreichte, plastisch wirkende Bilder, der räumliche Eindruck kann jedoch durch *stereoskopische Betrachtung geeigneter Bildpaare* noch gesteigert werden. Zu diesem Zweck sind zwei Aufnahmen des Objektes mit einer Kippwinkeldifferenz von 3 bis 12 Grad, je nach den Höhendifferenzen in der Präparatoberfläche, erforderlich. Einen praktischen Objekthalter beschrieben hierfür FECHER u. BLASCHKE (1968). Ein Goniometertisch (Abb. 41) ist für diesen Fall besonders vorteilhaft. Mit Hilfe eines Stereobetrachters vereinigt man das Stereobildpaar zum echten Raumbild. Das *Ausmessen von Höhenunterschieden* mit Geräten, die für die Photogrammetrie entwickelt wurden, ist prinzipiell möglich. Für eine Genauigkeit von unter 20% ist jedoch eine besondere Eichung der Vergrößerung und des Kippwinkels erforderlich. Weiterhin ist zu prüfen, ob Zentral- oder Parallelprojektion vorliegt, außerdem ist auf Verzeichnung des Bildschirmes zu achten (WEIMANN 1970).

Der Rastervorgang ist im Prinzip der gleiche wie beim Fernsehen, jedoch in der Regel wesentlich langsamer. Die meisten Abbildungen dieses Buches wurden mit 100 Sekunden Abtastzeit aufgenommen. In jüngster Zeit wurden neue Scanningspulen entwickelt, die es gestatten, auch mit Fernsehfrequenz abzutasten und am Monitor stets ein stehendes Bild vor sich zu haben. Dabei können die geringen Einbußen an Bildqualität durch bessere Kathodensysteme ausgeglichen werden. Man kann also nicht nur wie bisher Anfangs- und Endzustand im REM-Bild festhalten, sondern auch *Bewegungsvorgänge* untersuchen (HOLM 1972 u. a.). Als Beispiele kommen etwa Zug-, Scher- und Bruchuntersuchungen mit geeigneten Probenbühnen (Abb. 42) in Frage (DINGLEY 1969). Auch Insektenarten, die gegen Vakuum und Elektronenbeschuß besonders widerstandsfähig sind, können damit lebend untersucht werden (PEASE u. Mitarb. 1966).

Beim normalen Betrieb des REM steuert die *Anzahl der von einem Objektpunkt emittierten Sekundärelektronen* die Hellig-

As previously stated, when the primary electron beam, specimen and collector are correctly aligned, the SEM provides three-dimensional images of hitherto unobtainable quality, owing to the exceptional depth of focus. *Stereoscopic observation of suitable pairs of images* may result in further improvement. In this case two separate photographs of the specimen are required with a difference in tilt angle of 3° to 12°, depending on the differences in height of the surface structure of the specimen. A practical specimen holder for this technique has been described by FECHER and BLASCHKE (1968), and a goniometer stage (Fig. 14) may also be employed to advantage. A stereoscopic viewer merges the pair of images into a true three-dimensional image.

It is possible, in principle, to *measure differences in height* with instruments developed for photogrammetry. Special calibration of magnification and angle of tilt is required when an accuracy of better than 20% is required. In addition one has to consider whether the projection is central or parallel; distortion due to the display screen must also be taken into account (WEIMANN 1970).

The scanning process is fundamentally the same as in television, but usually much slower. Most of the illustrations in this book were taken with a scanning time of 100 seconds. Recently new scanning coils have been developed which permit scanning with television frequencies, leaving a stable image on the monitoring screen. This means that one can examine not only initial and final conditions but also *dynamic processes* (HOLM et al. 1972). Examples are fracture, shearing and fragmentation research on suitable specimen stages (Fig. 42) (DINGLEY 1969). Some vacuum-resistant living insect species can be examined in this way (PEASE et al. 1966).

In the normal mode of operation of the SEM, the brightness of a point in the picture is controlled by the *number of secondary electrons emitted from the correspond-*

41

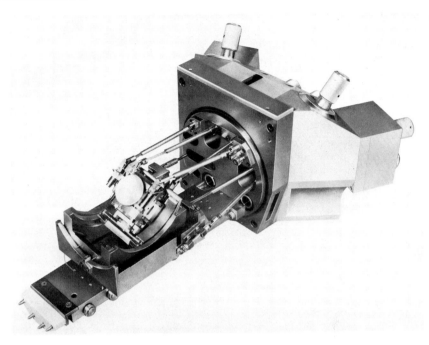

Abb. 41. *Goniometerbühne* zum Rasterelektronenmikroskop „Stereoscan". Probe bleibt bei Bewegungen der Bühne im Fokus des Primärelektronenstrahls.

Fig. 41. *Goniometer stage* for the SEM "Stereoscan" The specimen remains in the focus of the primary beam when the stage is moved.

42

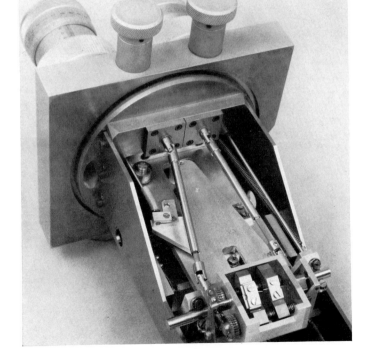

Abb. 42. Spezielle Probenbühne für Zuguntersuchungen nach *Dingley.*

Fig. 42. Special stage for tensile experiments after *Dingley.*

keit des zugehörigen Bildpunktes. Überstreicht der Primärstrahl eine bestimmte Strecke, so ergibt sich die Helligkeit der Bildpunkte als Funktion des Weges. Diese Funktion wird mit Hilfe des *Differenzierzusatzes* nach dem Weg differenziert. Man erhält so ein Signal, das nicht von der Helligkeit, sondern von den Helligkeitsschwankungen abhängt. Ein Beispiel zeigt Abb. 43b. Im Vergleich zu dem entsprechenden normalen Sekundärelektronenbild (Abb. 43a) entsteht eine ungewohnte Bildwiedergabe mit einer Überbetonung der Kanten und sonstigen Konturen, bei der der räumliche Eindruck weitgehend verlorengeht. Der besondere Vorteil der Differenziereinheit besteht nun darin, daß sie es erlaubt, das differenzierte Signal dem normalen zu überlagern (Abb. 43c). Auf diese Weise ist es z. B. möglich, den plastischen Tiefeneindruck mit einer schärferen Zeichnung der Konturen zu verbinden oder geringe Helligkeitsschwankungen in einer Fläche gleichmäßiger Helligkeit deutlicher hervorzuheben. Weiterhin wird der abbildbare Kontrastumfang wesentlich erweitert; Objektdetails in unter- oder überbelichteten Bildteilen gehen nicht mehr verloren. Im ganzen wird eine Verbesserung der Bildqualität erzielt.

ing point in the object. When the primary beam scans a given path, the brightness of the points forming the image is a function of the distance covered. By means of the *differentiating unit,* this function is differentiated according to the distance. In this way one obtains a signal which depends, not on the brightness, but on its fluctuations. An example is given in Figure 43b. In comparison with the corresponding normal secondary electron picture (Fig. 43a), the reproduction achieved here is unusual; the edges and other contours are too prominent and the three-dimensional impression is largely lost. The special advantage of the differentiating unit is that it enables the differentiated signal to be superimposed on the normal one (Fig. 43c). It is then possible, for example, to combine the impression of plasticity or depth with an intensification of the dilineation of the contours or to intensify slight brightness fluctuations in an area of uniform brightness. In addition the range of contrast is considerably enlarged; details of the object are no longer lost in under-exposed or over-exposed parts of the picture. On the whole the quality of the picture is improved.

Abb. 43. *Anwendung des Differenzierzusatzes.*
Objekt: Ca-oxalatkristall des Nierensteins.
a) Normales SE-Bild,
b) differenziertes Bild,
c) Überlagerung von a) und b).
Im Bild ist jeweils das Signal längs der geraden Linie einge-blendet.

Fig. 43. *Use of the differen-tiating unit.*
Calcium oxalate crystal of a renal calculus.
a) Normal SE picture
b) Differential picture
c) Overlapping of a) and b).
The signal is superimposed along the straight line in each picture.

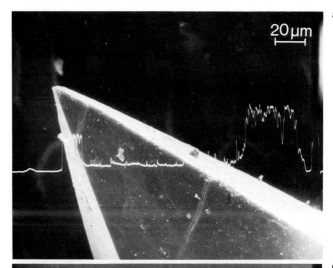

a

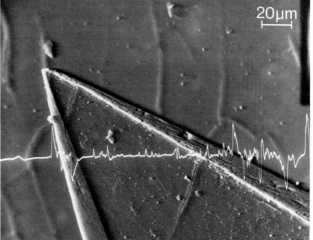

b

c

Materialdifferenzierung und Analyse

Infolge der Schärfentiefe wird man das REM bevorzugt dort einsetzen, wo es um die Abbildung rauher *Bruch- und Oberflächen* geht, die sich weder für eine Abdrucktechnik eignen noch direkt durchstrahlt werden können. Über die plastisch wirkende Abbildung hinaus wird sich häufig die Frage nach der *elementaren Zusammensetzung* der räumlich hochaufgelösten Strukturen stellen.

Zu einer Materialdifferenzierung im REM gibt es im Prinzip zwei Wege (HOLM u. Mitarb. 1969): Einmal kann chemisch durch Kontrastieren und Ätzen, zum anderen physikalisch durch Ausnutzen der verschiedenen Wechselwirkungen von Elektronen mit Materie eine Materialdifferenzierung herbeigeführt werden. Die Rolle der *Sekundärelektronen* bei der Helligkeitssteuerung der Bildpunkte auf dem Leuchtschirm kann sowohl von *reflektierten, absorbierten, durchgehenden oder Auger-Elektronen,* in derselben Weise aber auch von einer Anzahl *Photonen* oder von durch *Röntgenquanten* ausgelösten elektrischen Impulsen übernommen werden (vgl. Abb. 12).

Das Rasterprinzip erweist sich als außerordentlich vielseitig. Die Summe der Informationen durch die verschiedenen Wechselwirkungen zwischen Elektronen und Materie gestattet eine weitgehende Aussage über *Gestalt und Zusammensetzung* einer Oberfläche.

Bereits mit Sekundärelektronen und reflektierten Elektronen ist eine gewisse Materialdifferenzierung erzielbar, da das Reflexionsvermögen für Elektronen mit steigender Ordnungszahl der Elemente zunimmt. Die in tieferen Objektschichten reflektierten Elektronen lösen in der Oberfläche (Bedampfungsschicht) zusätzliche Sekundärelektronen aus, wodurch ein Materialkontrast auch im Sekundärelektronenbild möglich ist.

Eine völlig andere Art der Materialdifferenzierung liefert die *Kathodolumineszenz* (MANGER u. BESSIS 1970, HEYL u. HOLM 1970 u. a.). Von jedem Oszillographen und Fernsehschirm her ist bekannt, daß be-

Atomic Number Contrast, Cathodoluminescence and X-ray Spectra

In all the cases considered thus far, the SEM has been used purely as a microscope. Because of its depth of focus, it is applied above all to the imaging of *rough surfaces*. There is increasing interest in going beyond mere imaging to examination of the *elemental composition* of the surface. For this there are two main techniques (HOLM et al. 1969): Compositional differences of the surface material may be detected with SEM either chemically by selective etching and staining, or physically by exploiting the different interactions between electrons and the specimen. The function of picture brightness control can be assumed not only by *secondary electrons* but also by *backscattered, absorbed, transmitted* or *Auger electrons*. In fact we need not even confine ourselves to electrons; photons (cathodoluminescence) and electrical pulses generated by *x-rays* may serve the same purpose (cp. Fig. 12).

The scanning principle proves to be extraordinarily versatile; the combined information derived from the various interactions between electrons and sample material permits detailed analysis of the *topography and composition* of a surface.

To a certain degree identification of differences in material composition is already possible with secondary and backscattered electrons since the probability of backscattering increases with the atomic number of the element. The electrons backscattered from deeper layers of the specimen produce additional secondary electron emission from the surface (coating), which permits a display of material distribution in the secondary electron image.

Cathodoluminescence (MANGER and BESSIS 1970, HEYL and HOLM 1970, among others) offers an entirely different way of discriminating between materials. We know from oscilloscopes and television

Abb. 44a. *Sekundär-elektronenbild* eines Baumwolle-Polyester-Mischgewebes.

Fig. 44a. *Secondary electron picture* of a cotton-polyester mixed fabric.

44 a

Abb. 44b. *Kathodolumi-neszenzbild* des Präparates der Abb. 44 a. Baumwolle-Polyester-Mischgewebe nach einem Waschtest, bei dem nur die Baumwollfasern Weißtöner aufnahmen. Der Unterschied der Fasern ist im Sekundärelektronenbild (Abb. 44a) nicht erkennbar, im Kathodolumineszenzbild (Abb. 44b) dagegen erscheinen die Baumwollfasern weiß, die Polyesterfasern dunkel.

Fig. 44b. Same specimen as Fig. 44 a in the *cathodoluminescence mode of operation*. The cotton-polyester mixed fabric was subjected to a laundering test. Only the cotton fibers picked up the brightening agent. The difference between the cotton and polyester fibers cannot be detected in the secondary electron picture (Fig. 44a). On the other hand, with the cathodoluminescence technique (Fig. 44b), the cotton fibers appear bright, whereas the polyester fibers appear as dark shadows.

44 b

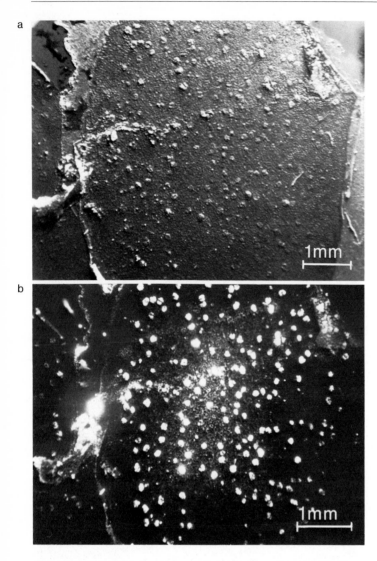

Abb. 45. *Kathodolumineszenz* an biologischem Gewebe (Ratten-niere). Vorbehandelt mit Fluoreszeinisothiocyanat angereichertem Antiserum.
a) Sekundärelektronenbild,
b) Kathodolumineszenzbild zeigt deutlich die Glomeruli.
(*W. Bröcker, E. H. Schmidt, G. Pfefferkorn* u. *F. K. Beller*, 1975)

Fig. 45. *Cathodoluminescence* on biological tissue (kidney of rat). The specimen was treated with antiserum enriched with fluores-cent isothiocyanate.
a) Secondary electron picture
b) Cathodoluminescence picture clearly showing the glomeruli.

stimmte Substanzen bei Beschuß mit Elektronen sichtbares Licht aussenden. Aber nicht nur die dort verwendeten anorganischen Kristalle zeigen Kathodolumineszenz, sondern ebenfalls eine Reihe organischer Farbstoffe, vor allem Weißtöner (Abb. 44a und b). Mit letzteren kann man andere Substanzen spezifisch anfärben und erhält einen Materialkontrast im rein organischen Bereich, unabhängig von der Ordnungszahl der Elemente. Man kann so eine Art Fluoreszenzmikroskopie mit der Schärfentiefe des REM betreiben.

Zwei der ersten Anwendungen der Kathodolumineszenz (KL) in der Biologie zeigen Abb. 45a und b sowie 46. Wegen der sehr schwachen KL-Signale wurde ein spezieller Spiegeldetektor nach HÖRL u. MÜGSCHL (Abb. 47) eingesetzt.

Alle bisher erwähnten Verfahren liefern über die Materialdifferenzierung nur eine *Orientierung für die Analyse, nicht die Analyse der Oberfläche selbst.* Erst durch Ausnutzung weiterer Wechselwirkungen zwischen Elektronen und Materie, der *Emission von Röntgenstrahlen* und *Auger-Elektronen,* ist eine *echte Analyse der Objektoberfläche* im REM möglich.

Die in einem Atom bei Anregung durch ein von außen kommendes Primärelektron ablaufenden Vorgänge sind schematisch in Abb. 48 dargestellt. Das Primärelektron erzeugt durch Stoßionisation ein Loch in der K-Schale. Das getroffene Atom kann die dabei aufgenommene Energie auf zwei Wegen (*Relaxation*) wieder abgeben: Ein Elektron aus einer weiter außen liegenden Schale (z. B. L-Schale) springt in die K-Schale; die dabei freiwerdende Energie wird als charakteristisches (K_α-)Röntgenquant abgestrahlt. Das Atom kann jedoch auch eine Neuverteilung der Energie derart vornehmen, daß ein weiteres Elektron emittiert wird. Dieser Vorgang wird nach seinem Entdecker *Auger-Effekt* genannt. Wird durch primäre *Ionisierung* eine Energie von weniger als 2 keV übertragen, so überwiegt der Auger-Effekt, sonst die *Röntgenfluoreszenz.* Die Wahrscheinlichkeiten für die beiden Relaxationsmechanismen bei primärer Ionisierung der K-Schale zeigt Abb. 49. Analoge Kurven gelten für höhere Schalen bei schwereren Elementen. Man erkennt, daß

screens that certain substances emit visible light when bombarded with electrons. Cathodoluminescence, however, is produced not only by inorganic crystals but also by some organic dyes (Fig. 44a, b), particularly optical brightening agents. These may be utilized to selectively stain other substances. This permits discrimination between materials in the purely organic field, independently of the atomic number contrast effect. It is therefore feasible to carry out a kind of fluorescent microscopy with great depth of focus in the SEM.

Two of the first applications of cathodoluminescence in biology can be seen in Fig. 45 a, b and 46. As the cathodoluminescence signals were very weak, a special mirror detector system according to HÖRL and MÜGSCHL (Fig. 47) was used.

All methods for discrimination of materials mentioned thus far serve merely as an *orientation for analysis and do not provide an analysis of the surface itself. Genuine analysis of the surface of the specimen* is not possible in the SEM unless further interactions between electrons and matter, such as the *emission of x-rays* and *Auger electrons,* are utilized.

Fig. 48 shows schematically the processes that occur in an atom which is excited by a primary electron from the outside. The primary electron creates a hole in the K-shell through impact ionization. There are two mechanisms of *relaxation* in which the atom concerned can release the energy thus absorbed. First, an electron from a shell lying further outside (e.g., the L-shell) may jump into the K-shell; the energy liberated in this way is emitted as a characteristic (K_α-)x-ray quantum. Second, the atom may redistribute the energy by emitting an additional electron, a process which is known as the *Auger effect,* after its discoverer. If the energy transmitted by the primary *ionization* is lower than 2 keV, the Auger effect predominates; if it is higher, *x-ray fluorescence* is predominant. The probabilities of the two relaxation mechanisms are shown for primary ionization of the K-shell in Fig. 49. Where heavier elements are concerned, the curves for outer shells are analogous. It will

TE

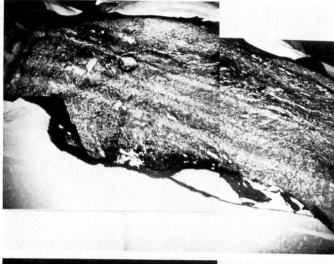

KL

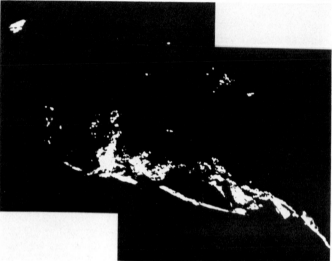

Abb. 46. *Transmissionselektronen-* (TE) und *Kathodolumineszenzaufnahme* (KL) am REM von einer Aortapartie mit Stenose.
(*W. Bröcker, H. J. Höhling, W. A. P. Nicholson,* Institut für Medizinische Physik, Universität Münster).

Fig. 46. *Transmission electron* (TE) and *cathodoluminescence* (KL) picture taken with the SEM. Specimen from an aorta showing stenosis.

Abb. 47. *Kathodolumines-zenzdetektor* nach *Hörl* und *Mügschl.* Das Objekt befindet sich im einen Brennpunkt eines elliptischen Spiegels, die Apertur des Lichtleiters im anderen Brennpunkt.

Fig. 47. *Cathodolumines-cence detector* according to *Hörl* and *Mügschl.* The specimen and the aperture of the light pipe are situated in the two focal points of an elliptical mirror.

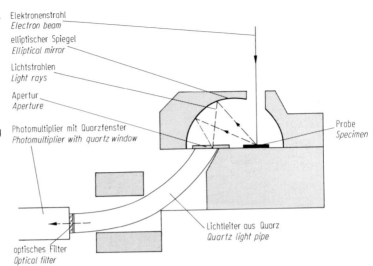

Elektronenstrahl
Electron beam

elliptischer Spiegel
Elliptical mirror

Lichtstrahlen
Light rays

Apertur
Aperture

Photomultiplier mit Quarzfenster
Photomultiplier with quartz window

Probe
Specimen

Lichtleiter aus Quarz
Quartz light pipe

optisches Filter
Optical filter

mit Auger-Elektronen alle Elemente (außer H und He, die nur eine Elektronenschale haben) nachweisbar sind, während sich bei der Röntgenfluoreszenz Schwierigkeiten bei den leichten Elementen ergeben.

Die *Spektroskopie der Auger-Elektronen* ist eine Oberflächenanalyse, die nur die obersten Monolagen der untersuchten Proben erfaßt. Dies erkennt man aus der geringen Reichweite von Elektronen der fraglichen Energie (≤ 2 keV) in Materie. Die Auger-Elektronen sind nur so lange analytisch verwertbar, wie sie die Probe ohne Energieverlust verlassen können. Die mittleren Austrittstiefen liegen in der Größenordnung 0,5–2 nm. Daraus folgt, daß die Probe unbedampft und nicht kontaminiert sein muß; auch dürfen während des Elektronenbeschusses keine Kontaminationsschichten aufwachsen. Letzteres kann man z. B. durch Spülen der Probe mit Argon erreichen (BRANDIS u. HOLM 1975).

Die kinetische Energie des Auger-Elektrons ist für das emittierende Element genauso charakteristisch wie die Energie bzw. Wellenlänge des Röntgenquants, d. h. beide Effekte sind analytisch verwertbar.

Die *Auger-Mikroanalyse* wurde bisher ausschließlich zu Untersuchungen an Metallen eingesetzt. Messungen an organischen Substanzen scheiterten an Zersetzungser-

be noted that all elements (except H and He, which have one electron shell only) can be detected by their characteristic Auger electrons, whereas difficulties arise with the light elements when the technique of x-ray fluorescence is applied.

Surface analysis by the method of *Auger electron spectroscopy* is applicable only to the outermost monolayers of the specimen. This can be seen from the fact that electrons of appropriate energy (less than 2 keV) have only a very short range in matter. Auger Electrons cannot be used for analysis unless able to leave the specimen without loss of energy. Their mean escape depths are of the order of 0.5–2 nm. It follows that the specimen must be uncoated and uncontaminated and that no contamination layers may be allowed to form while electron bombardment is in progress. Rinsing the specimen with argon (BRANDIS and HOLM 1975) is one way in which the latter requirement can be met.

The kinetic energy of the Auger electron is no less characteristic of the emitting element than is the energy or wavelength of the x-ray quantum; thus both effects can be used for analysis. *Auger microanalysis* has so far been used only to investigate metals. Investigations of organic substances have been prevented by decomposition phenomena because a specimen has

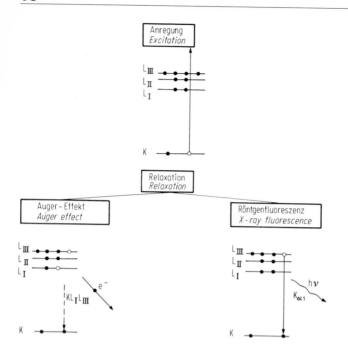

Abb. 48. Energieniveau-schema zur Darstellung von *Ionisierung, Röntgen-fluoreszenz* und *Auger-Effekt* (nach *Siegbahn*). Nach Anregung der K-Schale eines Atoms erfolgt Relaxation über Auger-Effekt oder Röntgenfluoreszenz.

Fig. 48. Energy-level diagram representing *ionization, x-ray fluores-cence* and the *Auger effect*. (From *Siegbahn*) After a primary ion impact has created a hole in the K-shell of an atom, relaxation by means of the Auger effect or x-ray fluorescence follows.

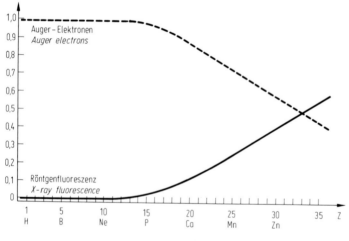

Abb. 49. Wahrschein-lichkeiten für *Röntgenfluo-reszenz* und *Auger-Effekt* als Relaxationsmechanis-men bei Ionisierung der K-Schale eines Atoms in Abhängigkeit von der Ordnungszahl.

Fig. 49. Probabilities of *x-ray fluorescence* and the *Auger effect,* as relaxation mechanisms following ionization of the K-shell of an atom, versus the atomic number.

scheinungen, da zur Erzielung einer ausreichenden Empfindlichkeit ein sehr intensiver Beschuß der Probe mit Primärelektronen erforderlich ist. Es sind jedoch erfolgversprechende Experimente im Gange, die Auger-Mikroanalyse auch bei niedrigen Primärstrahlströmen durchzuführen, so daß in absehbarer Zukunft wahrscheinlich auch organisches Material untersucht werden kann.

Somit ist die *Spektroskopie der Röntgenstrahlen* das zur Zeit einzige universelle Verfahren, das zur *Mikroanalyse in Kombination mit dem REM* eingesetzt werden kann. Sie kann prinzipiell in zweierlei Weise erfolgen: Zerlegen der Röntgenstrahlen *nach der Wellenlänge* oder *nach der Energie.* Das erstere Verfahren wird vorzugsweise im Elektronenstrahlröntgenmikroanalysator (kurz Mikrosonde genannt) angewendet. Das zweite, die *energiedispersive Analyse,* eignet sich besser für die Kombination mit dem REM. Sie soll deshalb ausführlicher beschrieben werden. Für einen Vergleich mit der wellenlängendispersiven Analyse sei auf Tab. 2 im folgenden Kapitel Leistungsvergleich verwiesen.

Bei der *energiedispersiven Analyse* setzt ein *Halbleiterdetektor* die von der Objektoberfläche emittierten einzelnen Röntgenquanten in elektrische Impulse um, deren Höhe proportional zur Energie der Röntgenquanten ist. Diese Impulse werden verstärkt und in einem *Vielkanalimpulshöhenanalysator* der Höhe nach sortiert, gezählt und gespeichert (Abb. 50). Nach einigen Minuten Zählzeit erhält man das *Energiespektrum der charakteristischen Röntgenstrahlung aller Elemente,* die in der vom Primärstrahl getroffenen Objektoberfläche enthalten sind (sog. *Punktanalyse,* Abb. 51a und b). Das Energieauflösungsvermögen moderner Halbleiterdetektoren liegt bei etwa 150 eV, so daß Elemente mit einer Ordnungszahl $Z \geq 9$ nebeneinander nachgewiesen werden können. Bei den leichten Elementen überwiegt der Auger-Effekt als Relaxation der durch Elektronenstoß angeregten Atome, so daß auch bei verbesserten Detektoren ohne Erhöhung des Strahlstromes die Empfindlichkeit um einige Zehnerpotenzen zu gering ist. Dazu kommt die Absorption durch das

to be bombarded very intensively with primary electrons to obtain adequate sensitivity. Promising experiments, aimed at the use of Auger microanalysis at low primary beam currents, are in progress; therefore, it seems likely that the method will soon be applicable to organic matter as well.

Hence *x-ray spectroscopy* is at the moment the only universally applicable procedure which can be used for *microanalysis in conjunction with the SEM.* In principle it can be performed in two ways, the x-rays being dispersed either *according to their wavelength* or *according to their energy.* The first of these techniques is used mainly in the electron microprobe analyzer (microprobe). The second technique, *energy dispersive analysis,* is more suitable for use in conjunction with the SEM and will therefore be described in some detail. Energy dispersive analysis is compared with wavelength dispersive analysis in Table 2 (see the following chapter, "Comparison of Performance").

In energy dispersive analysis an Si (Li) *solid state detector* converts the x-ray quanta to electrical pulses whose height is proportional to their energy. These pulses are amplified and fed to a *multichannel pulse height analyser* (Fig. 50). After some time of counting, the *energy spectrum of the characteristic x-rays of all elements* present in the area hit by the primary electron beam is obtained (point analysis, Fig. 51a, b). The energy resolution of modern semiconductor detectors is approximately 150 eV and therefore elements of atomic number $Z \geq 9$ can be resolved. In the case of lighter elements, the relaxation process produces Auger electrons rather than x-radiation, i.e., the sensitivity for light elements is too low by several orders of magnitude, even with increased detector performance, unless the primary electron beam current is increased. In addition, x-ray absorption in the detector protection window material also reduces sensitivity.

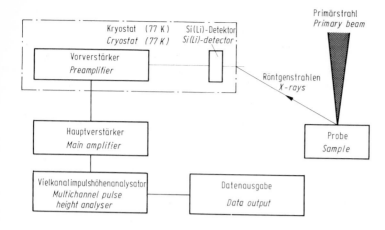

Abb. 50. *Energiedispersives Röntgenspektrometer* am Rasterelektronenmikroskop.

Fig. 50. *Energy-dispersive x-ray spectrometer* on the scanning electron microscope.

den Detektor schützende Fenstermaterial.

Mit 30 keV Primärstrahlspannung lassen sich die K-Spektren der Elemente mit Z = 11−40 (Na-Mo), die L-Spektren der Elemente mit Z = 25−92 (Mn-U) sowie die M-Spektren der Elemente mit Z = 72−92 (Hf-U) nachweisen. Wegen des begrenzten Auflösungsvermögens des Detektors kommen Überlagerungen von Linien vor. Da jedoch ein weiter Energiebereich von den L-Spektren der seltenen Erden eingenommen wird, sind sie in der Praxis nur selten störend.

Die besonderen Vorteile der energiedispersiven Analyse sind
1. hoher Wirkungsgrad des Detektors; es sind nur niedrige Strahlströme zur Anregung erforderlich,
2. simultaner Nachweis der Elemente; es wird kein Element übersehen und gleichzeitig Zeit gespart bzw. das Objekt geschont;
3. großer erfaßter Raumwinkel; dies kommt den häufig sehr zerklüfteten REM-Objekten sehr entgegen.
Die *Nachweisgrenze* für ein *homogen verteiltes Element* liegt etwa bei 0,1%. Auf diese Weise kann natürlich auch die Zusammensetzung einer Legierung schnell und genau ermittelt werden. Das Verfahren ist jedoch für solche Untersuchungen

With a primary beam voltage of 30 keV, one can detect the K-spectra of the elements with Z = 11−40 (Na-Mo), the L-spectra of those with Z = 25−92 (Mn-U) and the M-spectra of those with Z = 72−92 (Hf-U). As the resolution of the detector is limited, overlapping of lines occurs. In practice, however, this is seldom a disadvantage since the L-spectra of the rare earths occupy a broad energy band.

Energy dispersive analysis has the following special advantages:
1. High detector efficiency; low beam currents suffice for excitation.
2. Simultaneous detection of the elements; no element is missed, time is saved and specimen decomposition is reduced.
3. A wide solid angle is comprehended; this is a great advantage when, as is often the case, the surfaces of SEM specimens are very rough.
The *limit of detection* for a *homogeneously dispersed element* is about 0.1%. In this way, of course, alloys can be analyzed, but for such examinations other techniques can be more efficient.

Abb. 51a. Legierungs-
fremder Einschluß in
der Bruchfläche eines
Küntscher-Nagels.

Fig. 51a. Foreign body
inclusion in the fracture
surface of a Küntscher
nail.

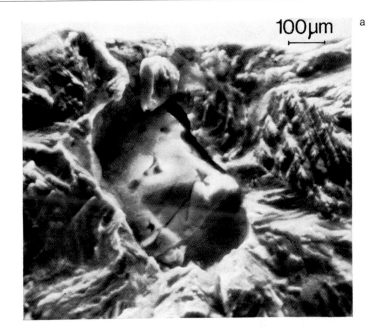

Abb. 51b. Energiedisper-
sive Röntgenspektren von
verschiedenen Bereichen
der Bruchfläche in
Abb. 51a.
Oberes Spektrum: Legie-
rung des Küntscher-
Nagels.
Unteres Spektrum: Le-
gierungsfremder
Einschluß.

Fig. 51b. Energy-disper-
sive x-ray spectra of dif-
ferent points of the frac-
ture surface in
Fig. 51a.
Upper spectrum:
Typical for the alloy,
Lower spectrum:
Foreign body inclusion.

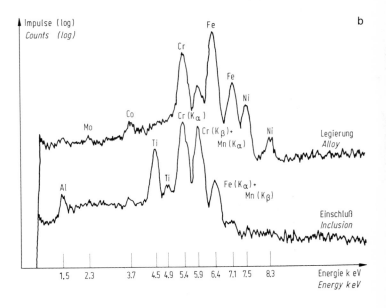

zu aufwendig. Man muß weiterhin berücksichtigen, daß nur eine Oberflächenschicht, die der Eindringtiefe der Primärelektronen entspricht, überhaupt erfaßt wird.

Der wesentliche *Vorteil der Kombination des REM mit dem Analysenzusatz* liegt in der Möglichkeit, inhomogene Elementverteilungen mit einem räumlichen Auflösungsvermögen zu untersuchen, das in günstigen Fällen unter 1 µm liegen kann. Zur anschaulichen Darstellung dienen *Elementverteilungsbilder* (Abb. 52 und 53) und *Linienanalysen* (Abb. 54b). Man geht vom integralen Röntgenspektrum eines Objektbereiches aus und wählt das Energieintervall, in dem die charakteristische Strahlung des gewünschten Elementes liegt. Im Elementverteilungsbild erscheinen dann die Bereiche hell, von denen Röntgenstrahlen der vorgewählten Energie emittiert werden. Bei der Linienanalyse erhält man die Häufigkeitsverteilung eines Elements längs einer Strecke (Abb. 54a und b).

Für Elementverteilungsbilder und Linienanalysen ist zu berücksichtigen, daß aus den Vertiefungen der Objektoberfläche nur wenige Röntgenimpulse in den Detektor gelangen, die entsprechenden Stellen daher im Elementverteilungsbild dunkel bleiben. Eine gewisse Anzahl Impulse ist für alle Objektoberflächenbereiche nachweisbar, sie wird auf die stets vorhandene *Bremsstrahlung* zurückgeführt.

Ein Beispiel einer Mikroanalyse an biologischem Material zeigt Abb. 55. Es handelt sich um Untersuchungen an der Bruchfläche (Gefrierbruch) einer Rattenleber (ZIEROLD 1975). Man erkennt einzelne Zellen (A) mit den runden Zellkernen sowie Gefäße (B). Die netzartigen Strukturen des Zellinnern beruhen wahrscheinlich auf Einfrierartefakten. Die an 4 µm² großen Arealen bei A und B gemessenen Röntgenspektren sind nebenstehend abgebildet. Die unterschiedlichen Verteilungen von P, S, Cl und K sind offensichtlich. Die Mikroanalyse wurde bei einer Beschleunigungsspannung von 12,5 kV sowie einem Probenstrom von 5×10^{-9} A durchgeführt. Um eine Verfälschung des Ergebnisses durch Diffusion zu vermeiden, wurde darauf geachtet, daß

It must also be borne in mind that only a surface layer, corresponding to the penetration depth of the primary electrons, is analyzed.

The real *advantage of combining microanalysis with SEM* lies in the opportunity to investigate inhomogeneously distributed elements with high spatial resolution. This, in favorable cases, may reach below 1 µm. Images of the *distribution of elements* (Fig. 52, 53) or *line scans* (Fig. 54b) can be obtained. One starts with the integral x-ray spectrum of a field of the specimen and selects the energy-band in which the characteristic radiation for the desired element lies. The element distribution image will then show brightly those areas of the image which emit x-rays of the characteristic energy of the desired element. In line scan analysis, the concentration of an element along a selected line is plotted (Fig. 54a, b).

Fewer x-rays, however, can reach the detector from low-lying regions of the surface of the specimen. These regions will therefore remain dark. A number of light spots are visible from all parts of the surface of the specimen, due to background radiation (*Bremsstrahlung*), which is always present.

An example of a microanalysis of a biological specimen is given in Fig. 55 (freeze-fracture surface of a rat's liver, ZIEROLD 1975). Individual cells (A) with the round cell nuclei as well es vessels (B) can be seen. The netlike structures inside the cells are probably due to freezing artifacts. The x-ray spectra measured on 4 µm² large areas at A and B are reproduced separately. The differences in the distribution of P, S, Cl and K are obvious. The microanalysis was performed at an acceleration voltage of 12.5 kV and at a primary beam current of 5×10^{-9} A. To prevent falsification of the result by diffu-

Abb. 52. *Elementvertei-lungsbild für Eisen.* Gleiches Präparat wie Abb. 51a. Der Einschluß ist eisenfrei. Die Untergrundimpulse rühren hauptsächlich von der Bremsstrahlung und der nicht ausgefilterten Mn (Kβ)-Strahlung her.

Fig. 52. *Fe distribution* in Fig. 51a. The foreign body inclusion does not contain Fe. The few spots in the area of the inclusion are due to the *Bremsstrahlung* and to Mn (Kβ) which cannot be resolved from Fe.

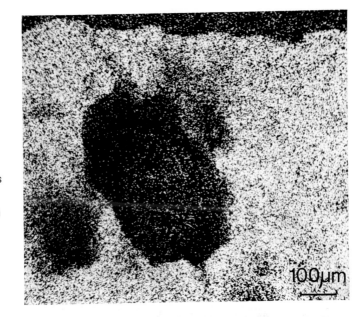

Abb. 53. *Elementvertei-lungsbild für Mangan.* Gleiches Präparat wie Abb. 51a.

Fig. 53. *Mn distribution* in Fig. 51a.

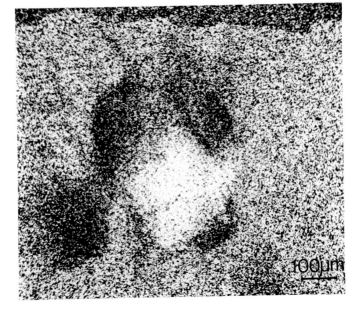

54a

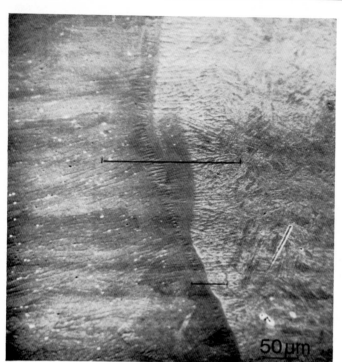

Abb. 54a. Angeätzter Schliff einer Schweißnaht im rasterelektronenmikroskopischen Bild.

Fig. 54a. SEM image of a lightly etched, polished section of a weld junction.

50 µm

54b

Impulse
Counts

keine Vermischung
no diffusion

5 µm

Impulse
Counts

Vermischung
Diffusion

20 µm

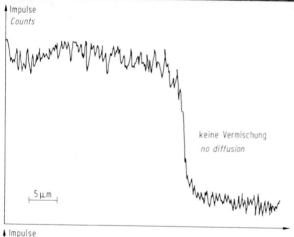

Abb. 54b. Die Cr-Linienanalyse über der Schweißnaht zeigt oben keine, unten deutliche Vermischung der verschweißten Teile infolge Diffusion. (Objekt der Abb. 54a.)

Fig. 54b. Cr line scan analysis shows regions without (above) and with (below) diffusion after the welding process. (Specimen as in Fig. 54a.)

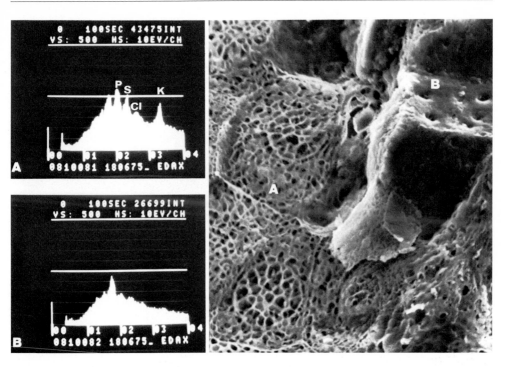

Abb. 55. Gefrierbruch einer Rattenleber. Rechts: REM-Bild. Für die Gewebebereiche A und B zeigen die energiedispersiven Röntgenspektren (links) unterschiedliche Menge von P, S, Cl und K an. (*K. Zierold u. Schäfer*, 1975).

Fig. 55. Freeze fracture of rat liver. Right: SEM picture. The energy dispersive x-ray spectra (left) show different amounts of P, S, Cl and K for the tissue regions A and B.

die Probe während der gesamten Präparation stets kälter als −110 °C blieb.

Es ist zwar jeder Punkt einer rauhen Oberfläche analysierbar, doch sollte man in ungünstigen Fällen vorsichtig sein (Abb. 56). Der zu analysierende Bereich sollte Sichtverbindung mit dem Detektor haben. Weiterhin muß man in Betracht ziehen, daß reflektierte Elektronen in anderen Probenbereichen oder an der Probenwand ebenfalls Röntgenstrahlen auslösen können.

Das räumliche Auflösungsvermögen ist im *Elementverteilungsbild* stets schlechter als im Sekundärelektronenbild. Dies liegt daran, daß von Materie Röntgenstrahlen sehr viel schwächer absorbiert werden als Elektronen. Auch bei fein gebündeltem

sion, the specimen was kept at a temperature below −110° C throughout its preparation.

Despite the fact that any point of a rough surface can be analyzed, care should be taken in difficult cases (Fig. 56). The region to be analyzed should have a direct line of sight to the detector. In addition it should be borne in mind that backscattered electrons may likewise release x-rays in other regions of the specimen or on the walls of the specimen chamber.

The spatial resolution is always poorer in the *element distribution image* than in the secondary electron image. This is due to the fact that matter absorbs x-rays much less powerfully than electrons. Even when the primary beam is focused to a

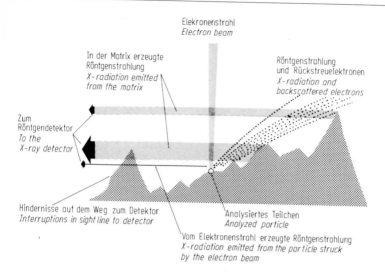

Abb. 56. Fehlermöglichkeiten bei der *Röntgenmikroanalyse an rauhen Probenflächen* (nach *Hantsche*).

Fig. 56. Opportunities for error in the *x-ray microanalysis of rough specimen surfaces* (from *Hantsche*).

Primärstrahl stammen die Röntgenstrahlen aus dem gesamten Diffusionsbereich der Primärelektronen und der reflektierten Elektronen.

Die Kombination REM und energiedispersives Spektrometer liefert zunächst nur qualitative Analysenergebnisse. Um zu *quantitativen Aussagen* zu gelangen, muß man die geometrischen Parameter bei der Untersuchung genau kennen, den Bremsstrahlungsuntergrund sorgfältig subtrahieren sowie die Eindringtiefe und Rückstreuung der Primärelektronen, die Absorption der Röntgenstrahlen in der Probe und Sekundärfluoreszenzbeiträge (auch von der Bremsstrahlung) berücksichtigen. Hierfür sind bessere Möglichkeiten sowie bereits erprobte Korrekturverfahren bei der *Mikrosonde* gegeben.

narrow point, the x-rays originate from the entire diffusion zone of the primary electrons and of the backscattered electrons.

The use of an energy dispersive spectrometer in conjunction with the SEM is normally suitable for qualitative analysis only. For *quantitative analysis,* one must be entirely familiar with the geometrical parameters of the investigation; the background radiation (*Bremsstrahlung*) must be subtracted in an appropriate manner. The penetration depth and backscattering of the primary electrons, the absorption of the x-rays in the specimen and the contributions of secondary fluorescence (also of the *Bremsstrahlung*) must be taken into consideration. The *microprobe* is more suitable for quantitative analysis and it offers proven correction methods.

Leistungsvergleich mit anderen Mikroskopen und Analysengeräten

Wie jede Untersuchungsmethode, so hat auch die Rasterelektronenmikroskopie ihre optimalen Einsatzgebiete und ebenso Grenzen ihrer Anwendungsmöglichkeit. Neben der genauen Kenntnis des REM und seiner Arbeitsweise ist es deshalb auch nötig zu wissen, wann eine Untersuchung sinnvoller mit einem anderen Gerät weitergeführt werden sollte. Aus der Tab. 2 ist ein ungefährer Leistungsvergleich der verschiedenen Mikroskoptypen zu entnehmen.

Muß eine Objektoberfläche mit einem räumlichen *Auflösungsvermögen besser als 20 nm* untersucht werden, so ist man gezwungen, einen Abdruck der Objektoberfläche anzufertigen (Replikatechnik) und diesen im Durchstrahlungselektronenmikroskop zu untersuchen. Dies bedeutet jedoch Verzicht auf Materialdifferenzierung und Analyse. Geräte wie EMMA = Electron-microscope-microanalyser (CHANDLER 1971) sind für die Untersuchung von

Comparison of Performance with Other Microscopical and Analytical Instruments

Like every examination technique, the SEM has an optimum field of application and also limitations. Therefore a complete knowledge of SEM and its mode of operation is not enough; one also needs to know when further examination with other instruments would yield useful information. Table 2 compares the performances of various types of microscopes.

If the surface of a specimen requires examination with a *spatial resolution better than 20 nm*, it may be necessary to make a replica and employ the *transmission electron microscope*. This means, however, that opportunities for analysis are lost. Apparatuses like EMMA = *electron microscope microanalyzer* (CHANDLER 1971) can

Tabelle 2 Leistungsvergleich der wichtigsten Mikroskoptypen
Die Leistungsgrenzen sind erheblich abhängig vom Probenmaterial und von der Präparationsart.
Table 2 Comparison of the various types of microscope
The statements depend considerably on the sample and preparation technique.

	Auflösungsvermögen *Resolution Limit*		Vergrößerung *Magnification Range*	Schärfentiefe *Depth of Focus*
Lichtmikroskop *Light microscope*	etwa *approx.*	500 nm	6 x – 1000 x	bei *at* 100 x: 2-3 µm
Rasterelektro- nenmikroskop *Scanning electron microscope*	besser als *better than*	10 nm	20 x – 20000 x	300mal besser als Lichtmikroskop *300 times better than light microscope*
Durchstrahlungs- elektronen- mikroskop *Transmission electron microscope*	0.5–0.2 nm		50 x – 500000 x	begrenzt, durch Schnittdicke, bei Abdruck theore- tisch wie REM *limited by section thickness; with replicas, theoretically similar to the REM*

dünnen Schnittpräparaten einsetzbar. Abdruckverfahren sind bei sehr differenzierter Oberflächenstruktur nicht immer möglich.

Stehen *analytische Fragen im Vordergrund,* so sind mit dem Halbleiterdetektor des REM nur die Elemente mit einer Ordnungszahl Z ≤ 9, also nicht die leichten Elemente wie C, O, N erfaßbar. Der *Elektronenstrahlröntgenmikroanalysator* ermöglicht auch eine Analyse dieser leichteren Elemente. Er arbeitet wie das REM nach dem Rasterverfahren und nutzt die gleichen Wechselwirkungen zwischen Elektronen und Materie aus. Da das Schwergewicht jedoch bei der Mikrosonde auf der Analyse liegt, müssen Einschränkungen in den Abbildungseigenschaften des Gerätes hingenommen werden (schlechtere Elektronenoptik, Objektschädigung durch hohe Strahlströme).

Einen Vergleich bezüglich verschiedener Leistungsdaten gibt Tab. 3.

Daraus folgt: Das *energiedispersive Verfahren* ist in den Fällen vorzuziehen, in denen eine schnelle qualitative Punktanalyse auf unebenen Proben bei niedrigen Strahlströmen gefragt ist. *Linescans* und *Elementverteilungsbilder* lassen sich besser mit der *Mikrosonde* aufnehmen. Dies zeigt eine einfache Betrachtung des Signal-Untergrund-Verhältnisses (Abb. 57). Eine

only be used to examine thin sections. Replica techniques, particularly with very coarse surface structure, are not always possible.

Where *analysis is of primary interest,* it should be noted that the semiconductor detector does not enable light elements with atomic number Z ≤ 9 (e.g., C, O, N) to be analyzed. With the *x-ray microprobe analyzer* ("microprobe"), however, even these lighter elements can be detected. The microprobe employs the scanning technique and electron beam specimen interaction in a way similar to the SEM, but the prime consideration is analysis and not imaging. Limitation in image formation due to inferior electron optics and specimen damage by higher beam current must be accepted.

The performances of energy dispersive and wavelength dispersive analysis are compared in Table 3. From this table and from what has been said above, it can be seen that the *energy dispersive method* is to be preferred where the requirement is a rapid qualitative point analysis of a rough surface at a low beam current. The *microprobe* is more suitable for *line scans* and *element distribution imaging,* as a glance at the signal-to-noise ratio shows (Fig. 57). An x-ray emission line

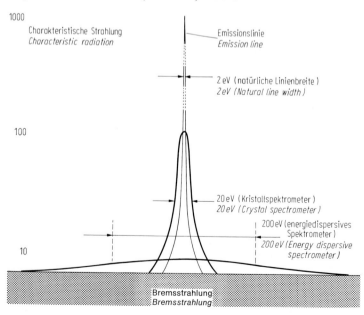

1000

Charakteristische Strahlung
Characteristic radiation

Emissionslinie
Emission line

2 eV (natürliche Linienbreite)
2eV (Natural line width)

100

20 eV (Kristallspektrometer)
20eV (Crystal spectrometer)

200 eV (energiedispersives Spektrometer)
200eV (Energy dispersive spectrometer)

10

Bremsstrahlung
Bremsstrahlung

Abb. 57. Linienbreiten und Signal-Untergrund-Verhältnisse bei energie- und wellenlängendispersiven Röntgenspektren.

Fig. 57. Line widths and signal-to-noise ratios for energy dispersive and wavelength dispersive x-ray spectra.

Tabelle 3 Vergleich der Leistungen des energie- und des wellenlängendispersiven
Röntgenspektrometers bei der Mikroanalyse

Table 3 Comparison of the Performances of an Energy Dispersive Spectrometer and a Crystal Spectrometer in Microanalysis

Leistungsmerkmale *Performance characteristics*	Rasterelektronenmikroskop mit energiediespersivem Si (Li)-Spektrometer *Scanning electron Microscope with energy dispersive Si (Li)-spectrometer*	Mikrosonde mit Kristallspektrometer *Microprobe with crystal spectrometer*
Energiebereich *Energy range*	$\geqq 1$ keV, $Z \geqq 11$	$\geqq 100$ eV, $Z \geqq 3$
Energieauflösung *Energy resolution*	~ 200 eV	~ 20 eV
Signal: Untergrund *Signal-to-noise ratio*	schlecht *poor*	gut *good*
Nachweisgrenze *Limit of detection*	normiert auf gleiche Anregungsbedingungen ungefähr gleich tatsächlich erreichbare Nachweisgrenze abhängig von Zählrate *approximately equal if instruments are standardized to equal excitation conditions; limit of detection actually achievable depends on count rate*	
Reproduzierbarkeit *Reproducibility*	in bezug auf Energie- und Intensitätsmessung gleichwertig *equal in respect of energy and intensity measurement*	
maximale Impulsrate *Maximum pulse rate*	10^5 Imp./sec (gesamtes Spektrum) *10^5 pulses/sec (entire spectrum)*	10^6 Imp./sec (einzelne Linie) *10^6 pulses/sec (single line)*
Wirkungsgrad *Efficiency*	90–100%	10–50%
mögliche Abweichung vom Sollkreis *Possible deviation from the Rowland circle*	groß, Gerät arbeitet weitgehend geometrieunabhängig *large; functioning of instrument is substantially independent of geometry*	klein, möglichst ebene Proben *small; specimens must be as plane as possible*
räumliches Auflösungsvermögen *Spatial resolution*		
Dünnschnitte *Thin sections*	30 nm (je nach Durchmesser) des Primärstrahles) *30 nm (depending on primary beam diameter)*	300 nm
massive Proben *Solid specimens*	1 μm	1 μm

Tabelle 4 Vergleich verschiedener Methoden zur Mikroanalyse
Table 4   Comparison of Different Methods for Microanalysis

	Röntgenfluoreszenz *X-ray fluorescence*	Auger-Effekt *Auger effect*	Sekundärionenemission *Secondary ion emission*
Prinzip *Principle*			
Anregung *Excitation*	Elektronen *electrons*	Elektronen *electrons*	Ionen *ions*
Information *Information*	Energie bzw. Wellen- länge charakteristi- scher Röntgenstrahlung *energy or wavelength of characteristic x-radiation*	kinetische Ener- gie emittierter Augerelektronen *kinetic energy of emitted Auger electrons*	m/e von positiven und negativen Ionen *m/e of positive and negative ions*
Nachweis von *Detection of*			
Elementen *elements*	ja, $Z > 3$ *yes*	ja, $Z > 3$ *yes*	ja *yes*
Isotopen *isotopes*	nein *no*	nein *no*	ja *yes*
Wasserstoff *hydrogen*	nein *no*	nein *no*	ja *yes*
Verbindungen *compounds*	in Sonderfällen Linien- verschiebung *line shifts in special cases only*	u. a. Änderung von Linienform und E_{kin} mit Bindungszustand *i. a., line shape and E_{kin} change with binding state*	Molekülionen und Bruchstücke *molecular ions and fragments*
erfaßte Schichtdicke *Analyzed layer thickness*	etwa 1000 nm *about*	0,5–5 nm	1 nm
Zerstörung der Oberfläche *Destruction of surface*	sehr gering *very slight*	gering *slight*	Abbau *decomposition*

Tabelle 4 Vergleich verschiedener Methoden zur Mikroanalyse (Fortsetzung)
Table 4   Comparison of Different Methods for Microanalysis (Continued)

	Röntgenfluoreszenz *X-ray fluorescence*	Auger-Effekt *Auger effect*	Sekundärionenemission *Secondary ion emission*
Nachweisgrenze *Limit of detection*			
in % des erfaßten Volumens *as percentage of analyzed volume*	10^{-1}–10^{-3}	10^{-2}	10^{-3}–10^{-7}
in Gramm *in grams*	10^{-11}–10^{-16}	10^{-11}–10^{-15}	10^{-15}–10^{-19}
unterschiedliche Empfindlichkeit für Elemente und Verbindungen *Sensitivity difference for elements and compounds*	Faktor 10 mit Ausnahme der leichten Elemente *factor of 10, except for the light elements*	Faktor 10 *factor of 10*	Faktor 10^3; bei O-Beschuß Faktor 10^2 *factor of 10^3; factor of 10^2 for O-bombardment*
quantitive Messungen *Quantitative measurements*	gut bearbeitet *good*	im Prinzip möglich *possible in principle*	nur bei Anregung mit O *only possible with O-excitation*
Analyse von *Analysis of*			
Isolatoren *insulators*	Bedampfung *vapor coating*	nur bei räumlich homogener Aufladung *only if specimen is homogeneously charged*	mit negativen Ionen *with negative ions*
Kunststoffen *plastics*	Bedampfung *vapor coating*	häufig Zersetzung *decomposition frequent*	? ?
räumliches Auflösungsvermögen *spatial resolution*	1000 nm	100 nm	2000 nm
Vakuumanforderung *vacuum required*	10^{-3} Pa	10^{-4}–10^{-9} Pa	10^{-4}–10^{-9} Pa

Röntgenemissionslinie hat eine natürliche Linienbreite von etwa 2 eV. Daraus macht ein Kristallspektrometer eine Linie mit einer Halbwertbreite von 20 eV, ein energiedispersives Spektrometer jedoch eine solche mit einer Halbwertbreite von 200 eV. Grenzt man das Energiefenster etwa bei den Wendepunkten der Linie ab, so sieht man, daß beim energiedispersiven Spektrometer prozentual weit mehr Untergrund (Bremsstrahlung) erfaßt wird als beim Kristallspektrometer.

Für eine *echte Oberflächenanalyse* (Analyse einzelner Atomlagen) sind jedoch weder das REM noch die Mikrosonde geeignet. Bei beiden Geräten ist die untersuchte Oberflächenschicht mit etwa 2000 nm für eine echte Oberflächenanalyse zu dick. Außerdem erhält man mit beiden Geräten nur eine Elementaranalyse und keine Aussage über den Bindungszustand der vorliegenden Elemente. Sollen derartige Probleme gelöst werden (z. B. Passivschichten auf Metallen usw.), helfen nur Oberflächenanalysenmethoden wie *ESCA* = Photo- und Auger-*E*lektronen*s*pektroskopie zur *c*hemischen *A*nalyse (SIEGBAHN u. Mitarb. 1967, HOLM 1971) oder *SIMS* = *S*ekundär*i*onen*m*assenspektroskopie (BENNINGHOVEN 1970). Ihr Einsatz bedeutet jedoch Verzicht auf Abbildungsmöglichkeiten.

Einen Fortschritt kann hier die *Auger-Mikroanalyse* bringen. Die Anwendung von *Ionenrastermikroskopen* wird für Biologie und Medizin erst in fernerer Zukunft möglich sein. Einige Leistungsdaten dieser Methoden sind in Tab. 4 der auf Röntgenfluoreszenz basierenden Mikroanalyse gegenübergestellt.

has a natural line width of about 2 eV. This is converted by a crystal spectrometer into a line with a full width at half maximum of 20 eV, whereas an energy dispersive spectrometer converts it into a line with a full width at half maximum of 200 eV. If the limits of the energy window are set approximately at the points of inflection of the line, it will be seen that the energy dispersive spectrometer takes in a far larger percentage of background (*Bremsstrahlung*) than does the crystal spectrometer.

For a *true surface analysis* in the atomic monolayer region, neither the SEM nor the microprobe analyzer is suitable. With both instruments a surface layer of approximately 2000 nm is analyzed, which is too thick for true surface analysis. Moreover, both instruments permit only an analysis of elements and reveal nothing about their chemical bonding. The solution of such problems (e.g., passive layers on metals, etc.) is possible only by methods of surface analysis like ESCA = photo and Auger *e*lectron *s*pectroscopy for *c*hemical *a*nalysis (SIEGBAHN et al. 1967, HOLM 1971) or SIMS = *s*econdary *i*on *m*ass *s*pectroscopy (BENNINGHOVEN 1970). Their use however, means abandoning the advantages of image reproduction.

Progress in this respect may result from the use of *Auger microanalysis. Ion scanning microscopes* are not likely to be used in biology or medicine except in the fairly distant future. Table 4 compares some performance data for these methods with those of microanalysis based on x-ray fluorescence.

Ausgewählte rasterelektronenmikroskopische Aufnahmen

Selected Scanning Electron Micrographs

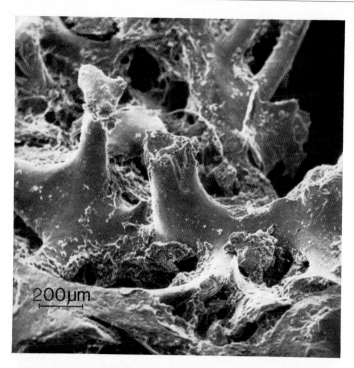

Abb. 58. *Spongiosa* des Hüftkopfes, Spülung in physiologischer Kochsalzlösung, Fixierung in gepufferter Glutaraldehydlösung, aufsteigende Alkoholreihe, Tieftemperaturbruch, C-Au-bedampft.

Fig. 58. *Spongiosa* of the femoral head. Rinsing in physiological saline solution, fixing in buffered glutaraldehyde solution, rising alcohol concentrations, low temperature fracture, C-Au-coated.

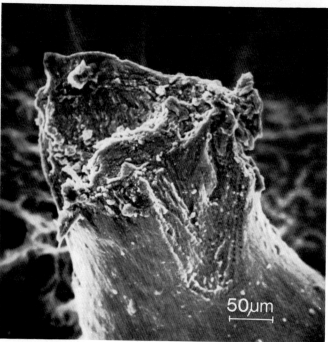

Abb. 59. Gebrochenes *Spongiosabälkchen* aus Abb. 58. Im schuppenförmigen Anbruch sind die lamellären Schichten im Inneren des Bälkchens erkennbar.

Fig. 59. Broken *bone trabecula* from Fig. 58. The lamellar layers on the interior of the trabecula are visible in the flake fracture.

Abb. 60. In der schuppenförmig angebrochenen Oberfläche des *Spongiosabälkchens sind Knochenlamellen und Fibrillen sichtbar.*

Fig. 60. Osseous lamellae and fibrils can be seen in the flake fracture of the *trabecula.*

Abb. 61. Von der baumrindenartigen *Spongiosaoberfläche* (rechts) dringen die *Fibrillen* in die darunterliegenden *Lamellen* (links) ein.

Fig. 61. The *fibrils* run from the treebark-like *surface of the spongiosa* (right) into the *lamellae* (left) lying below.

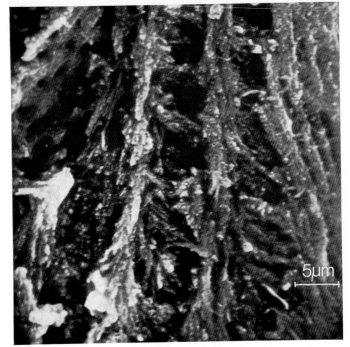

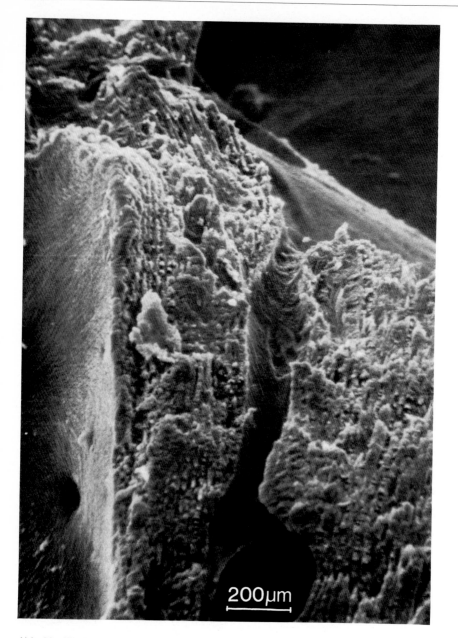

Abb. 62. Ein *Haverscher Kanal* (längsgebrochen) in der Kompakta des Oberschenkel-knochens mündet in den Oberschenkelmarkarm. Tieftemperaturbruch, C-Au-be-dampft.

Fig. 62. A *Haversian canal* (longitudinally broken) in the compacta of the femur open-ing into the medullary cavity of the femur. Low temperature fracture, C-Au-coated.

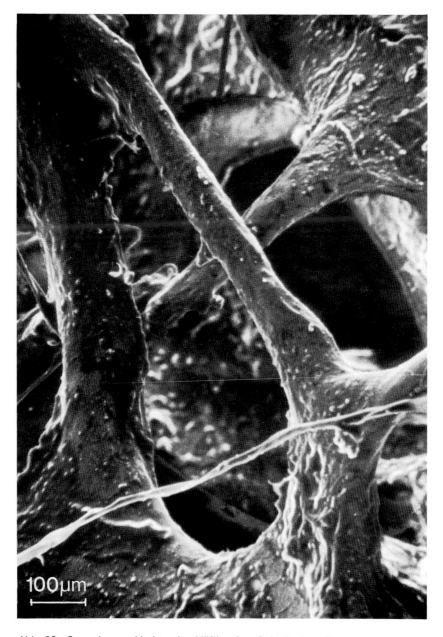

Abb. 63. *Spongiosaarchitektur* des Hüftkopfes. C-Au-bedampft.

Fig. 63. *Architecture* of spongiosa of the femoral head. C-Au-coated.

64

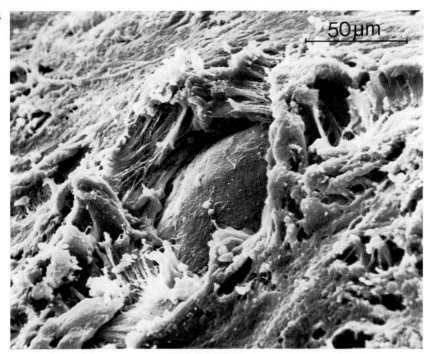

Abb. 64. *Hüftkopfarthrose.* Knorpeldefekte bis an die Knochen-Knorpel-Grenze rei-
chend. Mit physiologischer Kochsalzlösung abgespült, Fixierung in phosphatgepufferter Glutaraldehydlösung, aufsteigende Alkoholreihe, Exsiccatortrocknung, Au-bedampft. (*I. E. Richter,* Mainz)

Fig. 64. *Osteoarthritis* of the femoral head. Cartilage defect extending to the sub-
chondral bone.
Rinsed with physiological saline, fixed in phosphate buffered glutaraldehyde solution,
rising alcohol concentrations, exsiccator-dried, Au-coated.

Abb. 65. Hüftgelenkknorpel der Ratte. Durch Hyaluronidase freigelegte *Knorpelzell-* ▷
höhlen. 24 Stunden in 3,2%iger Hyaluronidaselösung in steriler physiologischer NaCl-
Lösung bei Zimmertemperatur fixiert, entwässert, exsiccatorgetrocknet, Au-bedampft. (*I. E. Richter,* Mainz)

Fig. 65. Hip joint cartilage of the rat. *Cartilage cell cavities* exposed by hyaluronidase.
24 hours in 3.2% hyaluronidase solution in sterile physiological saline at room temperature, fixed, dehydrated, exsiccator-dried, Au-coated.

Abb. 66. Freigelegte *Knorpelzellhöhlen* des Hüftgelenkknorpels der Ratte. Enzymati- ▷
scher Knorpelabbau durch Hyaluronidase. Au-bedampft. (*I. E. Richter,* Mainz)

Fig. 66. Exposed *cartilage cell cavities* of the hip joint of the rat. Enzymatic split of
cartilage by hyaluronidase, Au-coated.

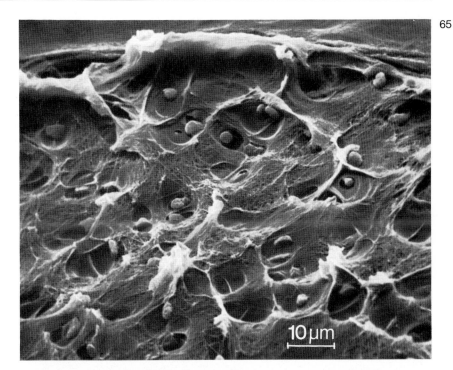

65

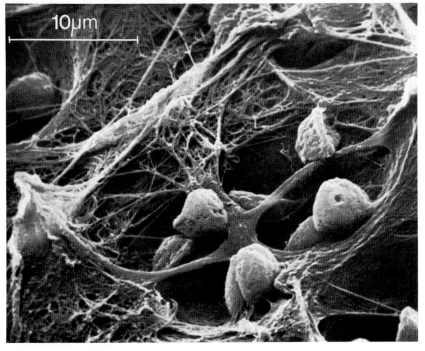

66

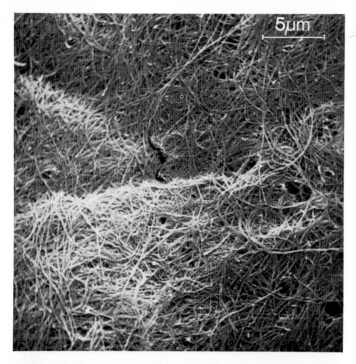

Abb. 67. Geflecht der kollagenen Fibrillen im Gelenkknorpel des menschlichen Hüftkopfes. Rechts: Gelenkknorpel, links: Hüftkopfspongiosa. In Jenkinscher Lösung entkalktes Präparat, sagittaler Tieftemperatur-bruch, C-Au-bedampft.

Fig. 67. Network of collagenous cartilage of the human femoral head. Decalcified in Jenkins' solution, sagittal low temperature fracture of femoral head, C-Au-coated.

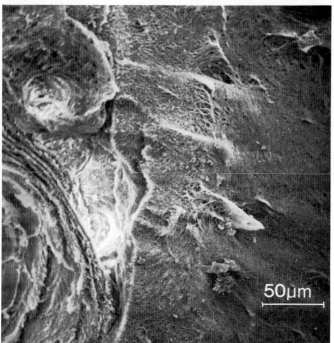

Abb. 68. Knorpel-Kno-chen-Grenze des Hüft-kopfes. Rechts: Gelenk-knorpel, links: Hüftkopf-spongiosa. In Jenkinscher Lösung entkalktes Prä-parat, sagittaler Tieftem-peraturbruch, C-Au-bedampft.

Fig. 68. Junction be-tween cartilage and bone of the femoral head. Right: articular cartilage, left: spongiosa of the femoral head. Specimen decalcified in Jenkins' solution, sagittal low temperature fracture of the femoral head, C-Au-coated.

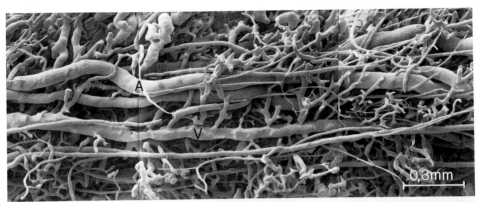

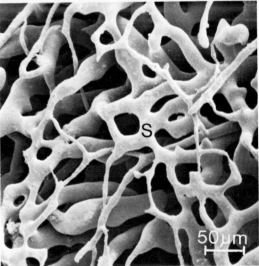

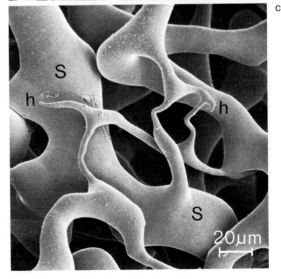

Abb. 69. *Gefäßsystem des Femurmark-raumes* der Ratte nach Gefäßfüllung mit Methylmethacrylat über die Aorta, Mazeration in konzentrierter heißer Natronlauge, Entkalkung in Plank-Rychlo-Lösung, OsO₄-behandelt.
a) Gefäßsystem des Femurmarkrau-mes mit Zentralarterie (A) und Zentralvene (V),
b) und c) Sinus (S) des Femurmark-raumes, angeschnittene Gefäße (h) zu den Haverschen Kanälen ver-laufend.
(*S. Irino, T. Ono, K. Watanabe, K. Toyota, J. Uno, N. Takasuki, T. Murakami*, Okayama)

Fig. 69. Methyl methacrylate replica of blood vessels of rat bone marrow. The lumina were filled with liquid plastic through the aorta, maceration with concentrated hot NaOH, decalcification with Plank-Rychlo solution, O_SO₄-treated.
a) Vascular system of the femoral medullary cavity with central artery (A) and central vein (V);
b) and c) Bone marrow sinuses (S), cut edges of veins (h) leading into the Haversian vessels.

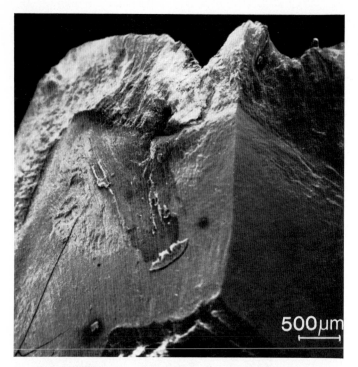

500μm

Abb. 70. Bruchfläche eines menschlichen *Backenzahnes.* Oben *Schmelz*, darunter *Dentin*, am Unterrand *Pulpa* eben sichtbar. Tieftemperaturbruch, C-Au-bedampft. (*H.J. Rehberg, R. Holm*, Bayer AG)

Fig. 70. Fracture surface of a human *molar tooth.* Above *dental enamel*, below that the *dentine*, on the lower edge just visible *dental pulp.* Low temperature fracture, C-Au-coated.

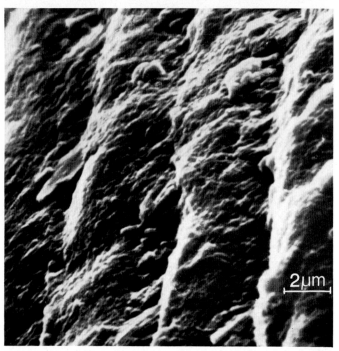

2μm

Abb. 71. *Schmelzprismen*, Ausschnitt aus Abb. 70. (*H.J. Rehberg, R. Holm*, Bayer AG)

Fig. 71. *Enamel prisms*, detail from Fig. 70.

Abb. 72. Dentin mit
Dentinkanälchen (längs-
und quergebrochen) im
schmelnahen Bereich.
Ausschnitt aus Abb. 70.
(H.J. Rehberg, R. Holm,
Bayer AG)

Fig. 72. Dentine with
dentinal canals (longi-
tudinal and transverse
fractures) near the den-
tal enamel. Detail from
Fig. 70.

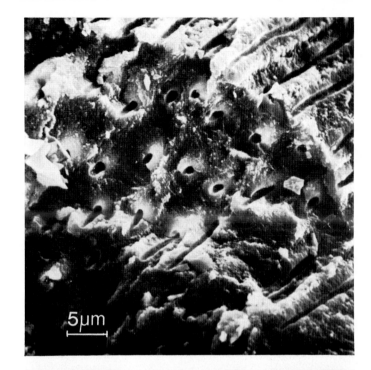

Abb. 73. Dentin mit
Dentinkanälchen im
pulpanahen Bereich.
Ausschnitt aus Abb. 70.
(H.J. Rehberg, R. Holm,
Bayer AG)

Fig. 73. Dentine with
dentinal canals near the
dental pulp. Detail from
Fig. 70.

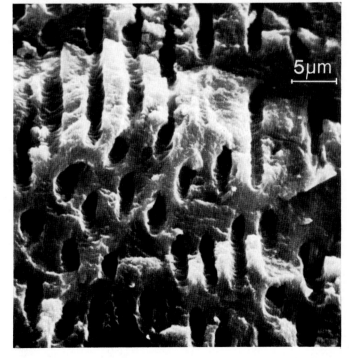

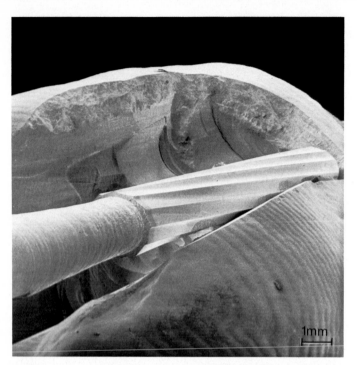

Abb. 74. Bohrloch im *Zahn* mit noch liegendem Bohrer. Au-bedampft.
(*A. Boyde*, London)

Fig. 74. Drill hole in *tooth* with drill. Au vapor-coated.

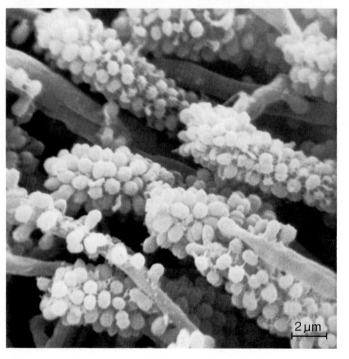

Abb. 75. Menschlicher *Zahnbeleg* mit maiskol-benähnlichen Bakterien-kolonien.
Fixation mit Formaldehyd, gefriergetrocknet, C-Au-bedampft.
(*S.J. Jones, A. Boyde*, London)

Fig. 75. Human *dental plaque* with bacteria colonies resembling corn cobs.
Fixation with formaldehyde, freeze-dried.
C + Au vapor-coated.

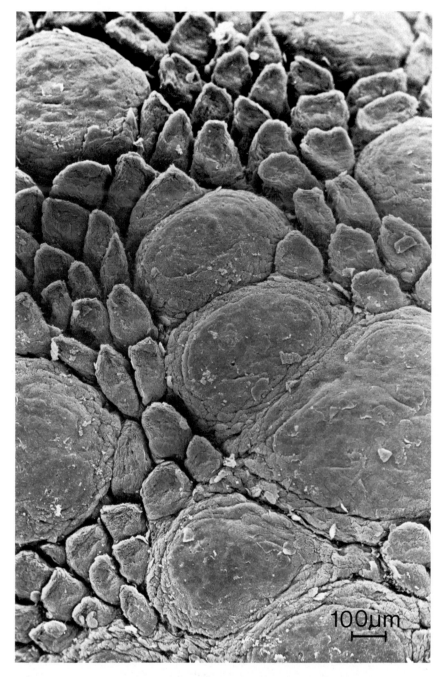

Abb. 76. *Kaninchenzunge* mit breitflächigen Papillae fungiformes und zuge-spitzten Papillae filiformes. Entwässerung in aufsteigender Äthanolreihe, kritische Punkttrocknung unter CO_2, Au-bedampft. (*L. Busch, W. Kühnel,* Aachen)

Fig. 76. *Rabbit's tongue* with broad-surfaced papillae fungiformes and pointed papillae filiformes. Dehydration in ascending ethanol concentrations, critical point drying over CO_2, Au vapor-coated.

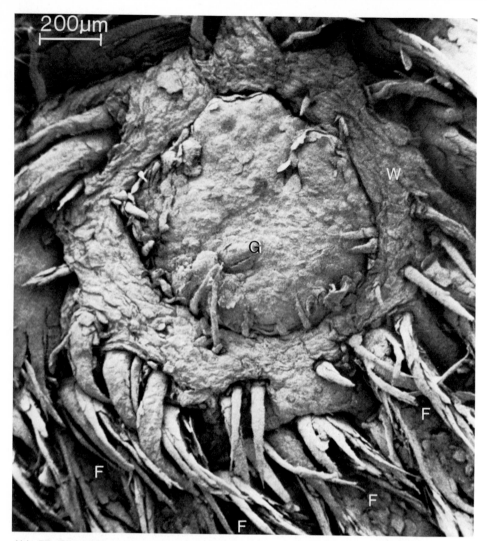

Abb. 77. Pilzpapille auf dem *Zungenrücken* eines Rhesusaffen. F = Fadenpapillen; W = Wall, G = Geschmacksknospe.
Fixierung in phosphatgepufferter Glutaraldehydlösung, aufsteigende Alkoholreihe, kritische Punkttrocknung, C-Au-bedampft. (*H.W. Beckers*, Köln)

Fig. 77. Fungiform papilla on the *back of the tongue* of a rhesus monkey. F = Filiform papillae, W = Wall, G = taste bud.
Fixation in phosphate-buffered glutaraldehyde solution, ascending alcohol concentrations, critical point drying, C + Au vapor-coated.

Abb. 78. *Kehlkopf* eines menschlichen Feten (♂ 21 mm SSL). a) Übergangszone zwischen ▷ Flimmer- und Plattenepithel im Bereich der Stimmfalte. – b) Ausschnitt aus der Übergangszone des *Kehlkopfes* (aus Abb. a). Plattenepithelzelle mit Mikrovilli, Flimmerzelle. Formaldehydfixierung, aufsteigende Alkoholreihe, kritische Punkttrocknung, C-Au-bedampft. (*H.L. Huenges*, Köln).

Fig. 78. *Larynx* of a human fetus (♂ 21 mm vertex breech length). a) Transitional zone between ciliated and non-ciliated cells in the region of the vocal fold. b) Detail of the transitional zone of the *larynx* (from a). Non-ciliated cells with microvilli interspersed among ciliated cells. Formaldehyde fixation, ascending alcohol concentrations, critical point drying, C + Au vapor-coated.

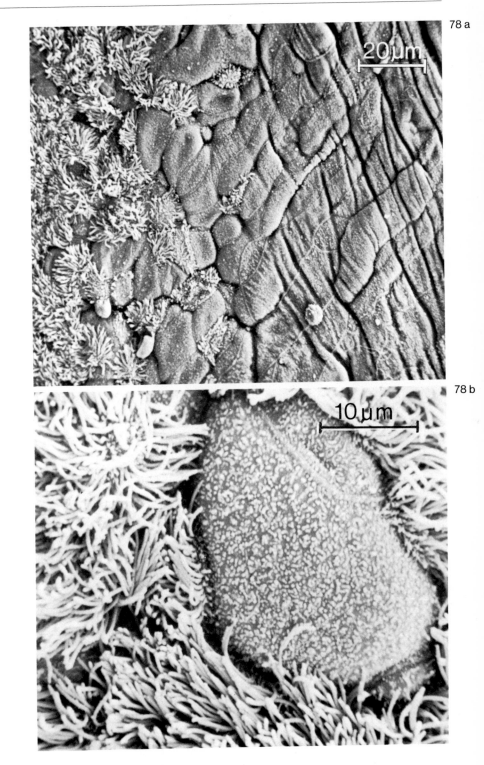

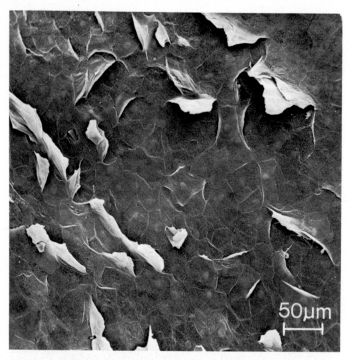

Abb. 79. Normale menschliche *Stimmband-oberfläche* mit sichtbaren Zellkernen und Zellgrenzen sowie physiologischer Abschilferung.
Fixierung in 5%iger gepufferter Glutaraldehydlösung, Entwässerung in aufsteigender Alkoholreihe, kritische Punkttrocknung über Amylacetat, Au-besputtered.
(*H. Lenz*, Krefeld)

Fig. 79. Normal human *vocal cord surface* with visible cell nuclei and cell margins and normal desquamation. Fixation in 5% buffered glutaraldehyde solution, dehydration in ascending alcohol concentrations, critical point drying with amyl acetate, Au sputter-coated.

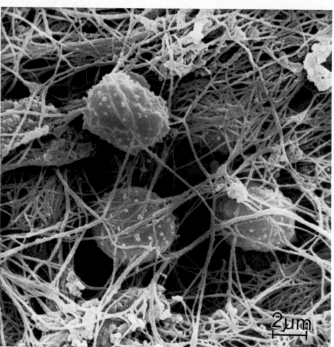

Abb. 80. Langzeit-Intubationsschaden an der menschlichen Luftröhre (Trachea): Drei Grundzellen im Fasergerüst der Basalmembran nach Ablederung der oberflächlichen Epithelschichten einschließlich des kinozilientragenden Epithels. Fixierung in 5%iger gepufferter Glutaraldehydlösung, Entwässerung in aufsteigender Alkoholreihe, kritische Punkttrocknung über Amylacetat, Au-besputtered. (*H. Lenz*, Krefeld)

Fig.80. Long-term intubation damage to the human trachea: three base cells in the fiber skeleton of the basal membrane after peeling off the superficial epitheliar layers, including the kinociliated epithelium. Fixation in 5% buffered glutaraldehyde solution, dehydration in ascending alcohol concentrations, critical point drying with amyl acetate, Au sputter-coated.

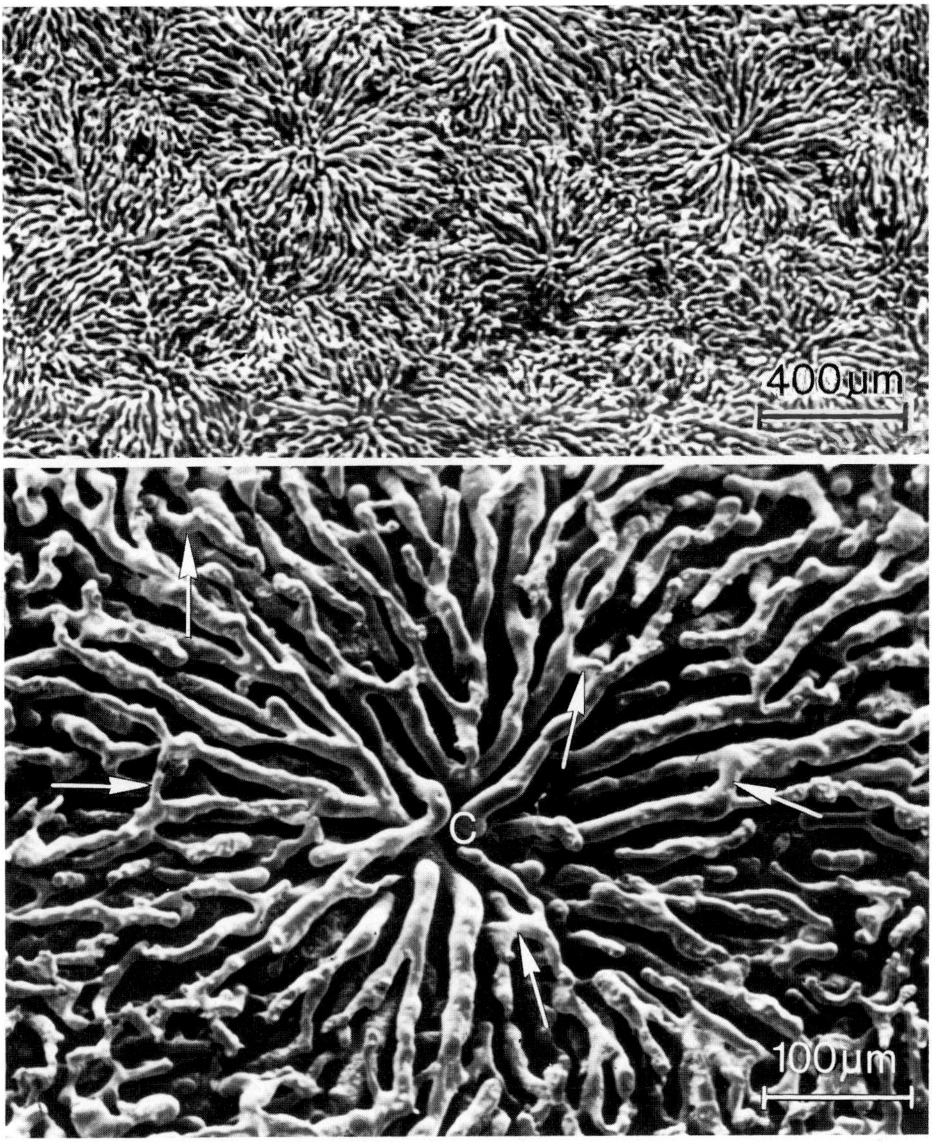

Abb. 81a und b. Gefäßnetz der *Rattenleber.*
Anastomosen der Sinussoide. Gefäßnetzfüllung mit Kunststoff (Technovit) und Mazeration der zellulären Bestandteile, Au-bedampft, C = Bereich der V. centralis. (*D. Schäfer, M. Seiffert, J. Höper*, Dortmund)

Fig. 81a, b. Vascular network of the *rat liver.*
Anastomoses of the sinusoids. The vascular network was filled with plastic (Technovit), maceration of the cellular components, Au vapor-coated. C = region of the v. centralis.

82

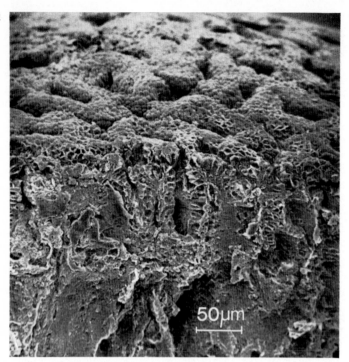

Abb. 82. *Magenschleimhaut des Menschen,* angeschnitten.
In physiologischer Kochsalzlösung gespült, in Formalin fixiert, in aufsteigender Alkoholreihe entwässert, Lufttrocknung, C-Au-bedampft.
(*I. Tautz, R. Holm,* Bayer AG)

Fig. 82. *Gastric mucosa of human,* section.
Rinsed in physiological saline, fixed in formalin, dehydrated in rising alcohol concentrations, air-dried, C-Au-coated.

Abb. 83. *Nierenstein* aus Kalziumoxalat, C-Au-bedampft. (*W. Ben-* ▷
der, R. Holm, Bayer AG)

Fig. 83. *Renal calculus* of calcium oxalate, C-Au-coated.

Abb. 84. Kristalline Struktur des *Nierensteins.* Objekt wie Abb. 83. ▷
(*W. Bender, R. Holm,* Bayer AG)

Fig. 84. Crystalline structure of a *renal calculus,* same sample as in
Fig. 83.

83

84

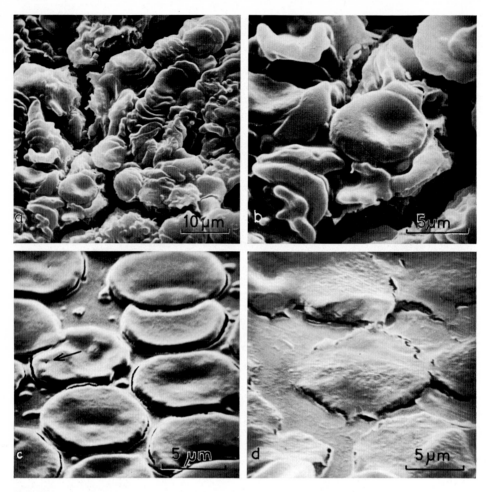

Abb. 85.
a) Unfixierter *Bluttropfen* luftgetrocknet; geldrollenförmige Aneinanderlagerung zahlreicher Erythrozyten.
b) Ausschnitt aus a). Nur mäßig erhaltener Erythrozyt.
c) Unfixierter Blutausstrich, luftgetrocknet (Routinemethode in der Diagnostik). Die Zellen sind sehr flach und wirken „durchscheinend", der Pfeil weist auf eine Pore.
d) Fixierung in ungepuffertem Formalin. Nach Auswaschen in Aqua destillata ausgestrichene Reste geplatzter Erythrozyten. (*I.E. Richter,* Mainz)

Fig. 85.
a) Unfixed *blood droplet,* air-dried; erythrocytes stacked together like coins.
b) Detail from a). Only one reasonably preserved erythrocyte.
c) Unfixed blood smear, air-dried (routine lab. method). The cells are very flat and seem "translucent", the arrow points to a pore.
d) Fixed in unbuffered formalin. After rinsing with aqua dest. flattened ghosts of destroyed erythrocytes are visible.

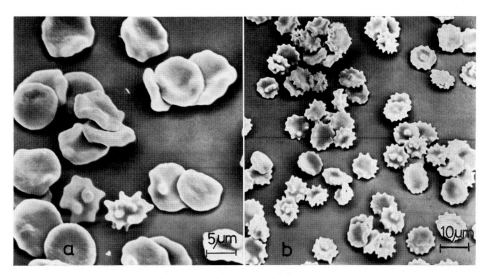

Abb. 86a und b. Formänderung von *Erythrozyten* nach kurzer Einwirkung einer 1%igen NaCl-Lösung (a) und einer 5%igen NaCl-Lösung (b) in vitro. (*I.E. Richter,* Mainz)

Fig. 86a and b. Alteration of the *erythrocytes'* shape after short exposure in 1% NaCl solution (a) and a 5% NaCl solution (b) in vitro.

Abb. 87. *Normale Erythrozyten* nach Fixierung in Glutaraldehyd, ausgewaschen in Aqua bidestillata. (*I.E. Richter,* Mainz)

Fig. 87. *Normal looking erythrocytes* after fixation in glutaralehyde, washed in aqua bidest.

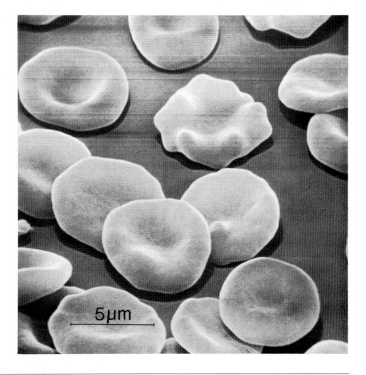

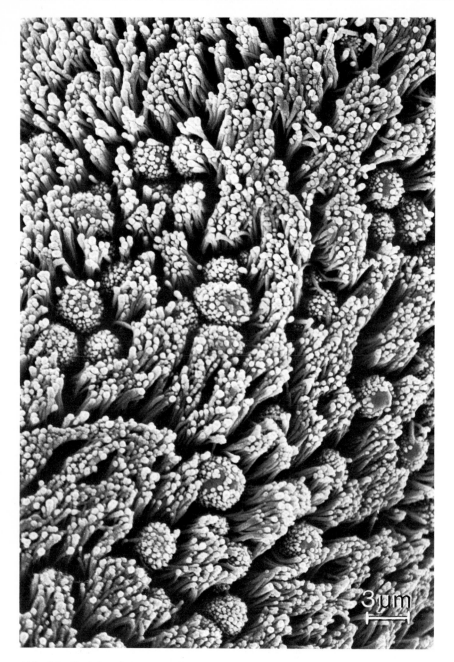

Abb. 88. Fimbrientrichter der *Tuba uterina* (Kaninchen) mit dichtem Besatz von Zilienzellen, zwischen denen vereinzelt Drüsenzellen mit stummelförmigen Mikrovilli vorkommen. Entwässerung in aufsteigender Azetonreihe, kritische Punkttrocknung über CO_2, Au-bedampft. (*L. Busch, W. Kühnel,* Aachen)

Fig. 88. Fimbrial infundibulum of the *tuba uterina* (rabbit) with a dense covering of ciliar cells, among which isolated glandular cells with stumplike microvilli occur. Dehydration in ascending acetone concentrations, critical point drying with CO_2, Au vapor-coated.

Abb. 89. Schleimhaut des *Kaninchenuterus* im Östrus. Kavumepithelzellen teilweise glatt, stellenweise mit stummelförmigen Mikrovilli besetzt. In Bildmitte zwei Zilienzellen.
Entwässerung in aufsteigender Azetonreihe, kritische Punkttrocknung über CO_2, Au-bedampft.
(*L. Busch, W. Kühnel,* Aachen)

Fig. 89. Mucosa of a *rabbit's uterus* in the estrus. Cavum epithelial cells, partly smooth and partly occupied by stumplike microvilli. Two ciliar cells can be seen at the center of the picture. Dehydration in ascending acetone concentrations, critical point drying with CO_2, Au vapor-coated.

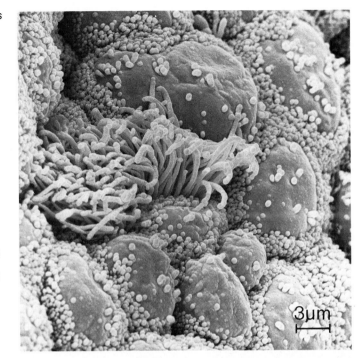

Abb. 90. Blutgefäß aus dem *Endometrium.* Aufsicht auf die polygonalen Endothelzellen mit flachen, leicht prominenten Kernen. Im Bild unten Abgang eines Gefäßes; in unmittelbarer Nachbarschaft liegen zwei Erytrhozyten.
Entwässerung in aufsteigender Azetonreihe, kritische Punkttrocknung über CO_2, Au-bedampft.
(*L. Busch, W. Kühnel,* Aachen)

Fig. 90. Blood vessel from the *endometrium.* Plan view of the polygonal endothelial cells with flat and slightly prominent nuclei. The junction of a vessel can be seen at the bottom of the picture; there are two erythrocytes in the immediate vicinity. Dehydration in ascending acetone concentrations, critical point drying with CO_2, Au vapor-coated.

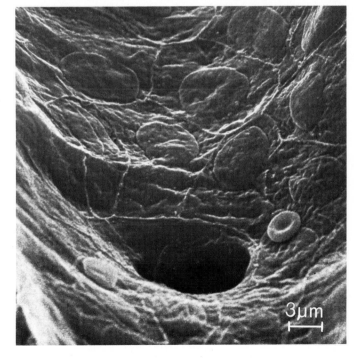

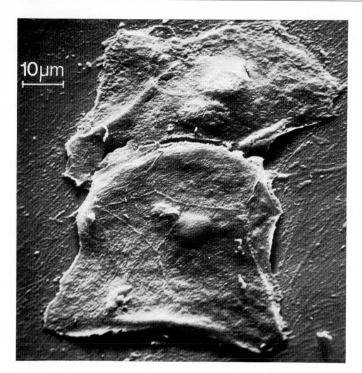

Abb. 91. *Portiozellen,* Abstrich auf Glasobjekt-träger. In aufsteigender Alkoholreihe entwässert, C-Au-bedampft.

Fig. 91. *Cervical endo-thelial cells* smeared on glass slide. Dehydrated in rising alcohol concen-trations, C-Au-coated.

Abb. 92. *Candida albicans* auf abgeschilfertem Vaginalepithel des ▷ Menschen. Lockere Anlagerung von Sproßzellen und Pseudomyzel an die Epithelzelle. Außerdem verschiedene Bakterienformen. Abstrich, entwässert über aufsteigende Alkoholreihe, kritische Punkttrocknung mit Freon, Au-besputtered. (*J.D. Schnell,* Düssel-dorf; *R. Holm,* Bayer AG)

Fig. 92. *Candida albicans* on desquamated vaginal epithelium of a human. Loose attachment of bud cells and pseudomycelium to the epitheliar cell. A variety of bacterial forms can also be seen. Smear, dehydrated over ascending alcohol concentrations, critical point drying with Freon, Au sputter-coated.

Abb. 93. *Candida albicans,* Kulturabstrich, entwässert in aufstei- ▷ gender Alkoholreihe, kritische Punkttrocknung mit Freon, Au-be-sputtered. (*J.D. Schnell,* Düsseldorf; *R. Holm,* Bayer AG)

Fig. 93. *Candida albicans.* Culture smear dehydrated in ascending alcohol concentrations, critical point drying with Freon, Au sputter-coated.

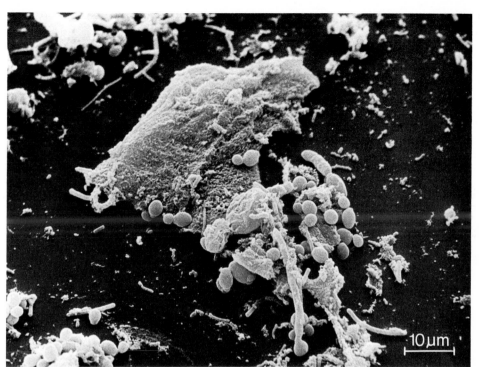

92

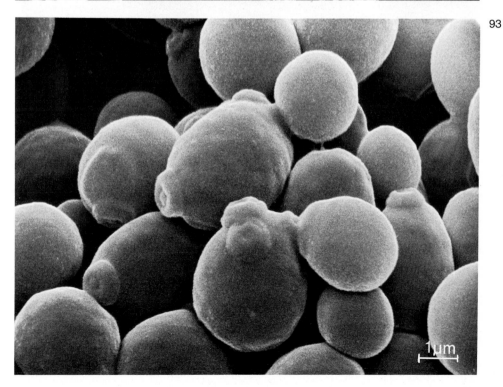

93

a

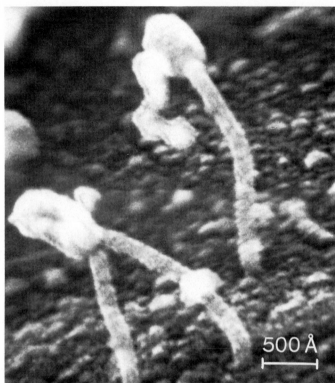

b

Abb. 94. *Bakteriophagen* auf Bakterien.
a) 3C-Phagen auf Staphylococcus aureus,
b) T4-Phagen auf Escherichia coli.
Fixation mit Glutaraldehyd und OSO_4, Kontrastierung mit Uranylazetat, Trocknung am kritischen Punkt, Bedampfung mit C + Au-Pd (sehr dünne Bedampfungsschicht, etwa 50 Å).
Die extrem hohe Auflösung (Endvergrößerung 300 000-fach) wurde mit einem bei IBM gebauten Versuchsgerät mit LaB_6-Kathode, kurzbrennweitiger Objektivlinse und Energiefilterung der rückgestreuten Elektronen aufgenommen.
(*A.N. Broers,* Yorktown Heights; *B.J. Panessa, J.F. Gennaro* jr., (New York)

Fig. 94. *Bacteriophages* on bacteria.
a) 3C-phages on Staphylococcus aureus,
b) T4-phages on Escherichia coli.
Fixation with glutaraldehyde and OsO_4, contrasting with uranyl acetate, critical point drying, coating with C + Au-Pd (very thin vapor coating of about 50 Å was used). The extremely high resolution was obtained in an experimental SEM, built by IBM, with LaB_6 cathode and short focal length final lens and energy filtering of the low loss backscattered electrons.

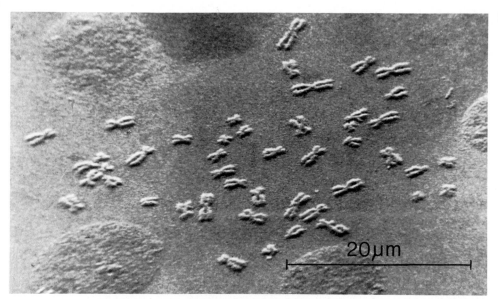

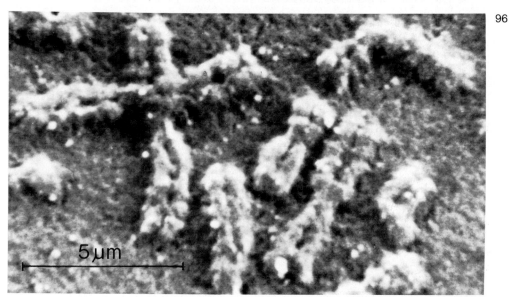

Abb. 95. *Chromosomen* eines Patienten mit Trisomie 21–22 (Mongolismus). Proteolyse: 250 γ Trypsin/300 ml Pufferlösung, 15 min. (*I.H. Pawlowitzki, R. Blaschke, R. Christenhuss;* Münster)

Fig. 95. *Chromosome set* of a patient with trisomy 21–22 (mongolism). Proteolysis: 250 γ trypsin/300 ml buffered solution, 15 min.

Abb. 96. *Chromosomenbild.* Knotenförmige Gliederung der Chromatiden. Ausschnitt aus einer Metaphasenplatte. Proteolyse: 1 mg Trypsin/300 ml Pufferlösung. (*I.H. Pawlowitzki, R. Blaschke, R. Christenhuss;* Münster)

Fig. 96. *Chromosomes,* knotted structure of the chromatids. Part of a metaphase plate. Proteolysis: 1 mg trypsin/300 ml buffered solution.

97

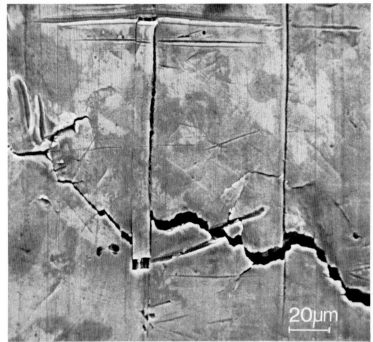

20µm

98

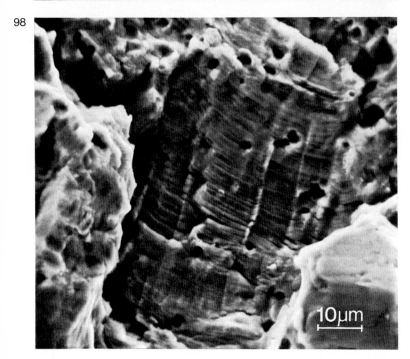

10µm

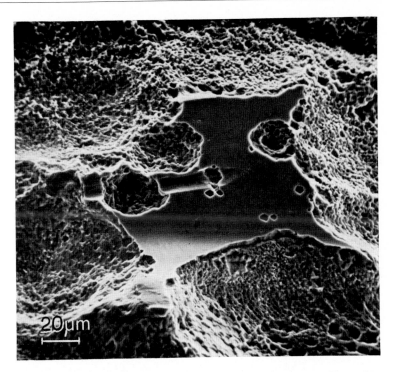

Abb. 99. Korrosion an der Oberfläche eines Metallimplantates führt zu erheblichem Substanzverlust des Metalls. Deutlicher Höhenunterschied zwischen inselförmiger, noch unbeschädigter Metalloberfläche und korrodierter Umgebung. Rostfreier Stahl. 12 Monate implantiert, ultraschallgereinigt.

Fig. 99. Corrosion on the surface of a metal implant leads to considerable loss of metal. Significant difference in height between island-shaped still undamaged metal surface and corroded surroundings. Stainless steel, 12 months after implantation, ultrasonically cleaned.

◁ Abb. 97. Feiner *Anriß* in der Oberfläche eines *Küntscher-Nagels,* Rostfreier Stahl. Ultraschall-Reinigung, unbedampft.

Fig. 97. Fine crack in the surface of a *Küntscher nail.* Stainless steel. Ultrasonically cleaned, uncoated.

◁ Abb. 98. *Rastlinien* des Dauerbruches. In der Bruchfläche des *Metallimplantates* beginnender Lochfraß. Rostfreier Stahl. Ultraschall-Reinigung, unbedampft.

Fig. 98. *Arrest lines* of a fatigue fracture. Pitting corrosion is starting in the fracture surface of the *metal implant.* Stainless steel. Ultrasonically cleaned, uncoated.

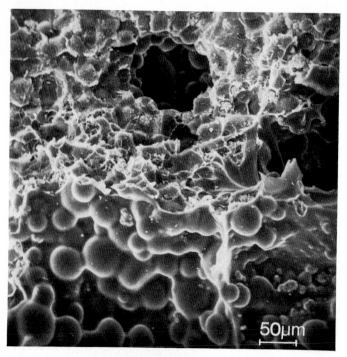

Abb. 100. Ausgehärteter Knochenzement *Palacos* Polymethylmethakrylat), Tieftemperaturbruch. Dabei werden einzelne Mikroporen im Inneren der Palacosmasse sichtbar, an deren Wänden Palacos-Pulverkörner erkennbar sind. C-Au-bedampft.

Fig. 100. Hardened *Palacos* (polymethylmethacrylate) bone cement. Low temperature fracture, several micropores in the Palacos mass rendering visible. Palacos powder grains are seen on the walls of the micropores. C-Au-coated.

Abb. 101. *Spongiosabälkchen* in Kontakt mit ausgehärtetem Knochenzement Palacos. Aufsteigende Alkoholreihe, Tieftemperaturbruch, C-Au-bedampft.
(*F. Meschede, H. Vogel,* Köln; *R. Holm,* Bayer AG)

Fig. 101. *Spongiosa trabecula* in contact with hardened Palacos bone cement. Low-temperature fracture. Ascending alcohol concentrations, C + Au vapor-coated.

Abb. 102. *Radiolarie* aus
dem Indischen Ozean,
Au-bedampft.
(*J. G. Helmcke,* Berlin)

Fig. 102. *Radiolar* from
the Indian Ocean. Au
vapor-coated.

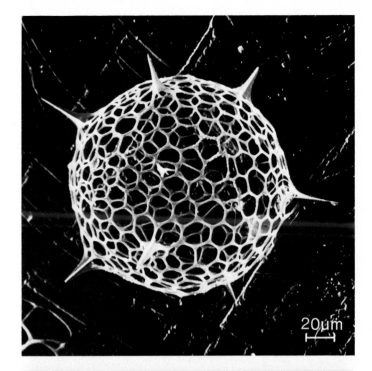

Abb. 103. *Radiolarie* aus
dem Indischen Ozean,
Au-bedampft.
(*J.G. Helmcke,* Berlin)

Fig. 103. *Radiolar* from
the Indian Ocean. Au
vapor-coated.

104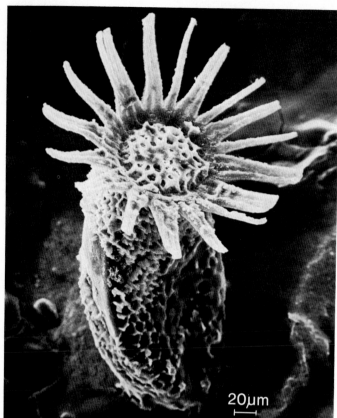

Abb. 104. *Wanzenei.*
(*U. Spormann*, Münster)

Fig. 104. *Egg of a bug.*

Abb. 105. Äußere *Scha-lenhaut* eines *Hühnereis.*
(*U. Derpmann*, Münster)

Fig. 105. Exterior aspect of a *shell* of a *chicken egg.*

Abb. 106. Behaarung des ▷
Kopfteiles einer amerika-nischen *Wolfsspinne*
(Pardosa lapidicina).
C-Au-bedampft.
(*R.F. Foelix*, Bochum)

Fig. 106. Hair on the head of an American *wolf spider* (Pardosa lapidi-cina)
C + Au vapor-coated.

Abb. 107. Haare der ▷
amerikanischen *Wolfs-spinne* (Pardosa lapidi-cina). Ausschnitt aus
Abb. 106. (*R.F. Foelix*,
Bochum)

Fig. 107. Hair of the American wolf spider (Pardosa lapidicina), detail from Figure 106.

20µm

105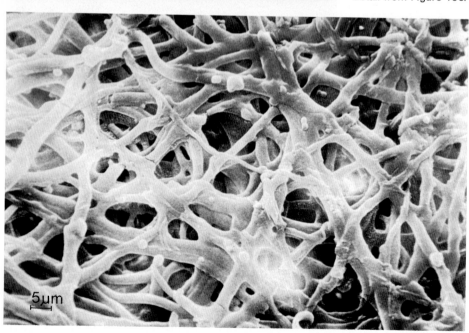

5µm

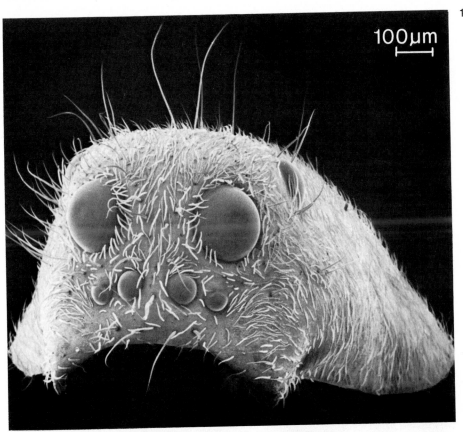

106

100µm

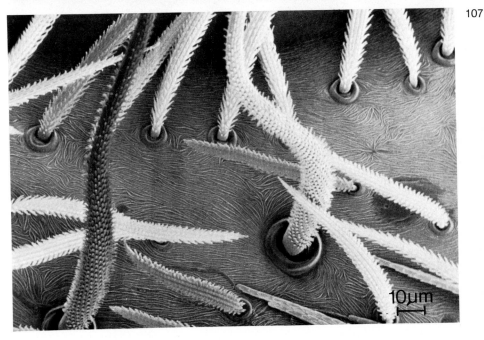

107

10µm

200µm

Abb. 108. *Bandwurm*
(Hymenolepis nana).
Übersicht mit Scolex
und Proglottiden.
Gefriertrocknung, C-
Au-bedampft.
(*H.P. Schulz, R. Holm,*
Bayer AG)

Fig. 108. *Tapeworm*
(Hymenolepis nana).
Total view with scolex
and proglottides.
Freeze-dried, C-Au-
coated.

200µm

Abb. 109. Verschlungene
Segmente des *Band-
wurms.*
(*H.P. Schulz, R. Holm,*
Bayer AG)

Fig. 109. Twisted seg-
ments of the *tapeworm.*

Abb. 110. Kopf des
Bandwurmes Hymenole-
pis nana. Vorderende
(Scolex) mit vier Saug-
näpfen und dem Haken-
kreuz auf einem aus-
stülpbaren Rüssel
(Rostellum). Saugnäpfe
und Hakenkranz dienen
als Befestigungsorgane,
mit denen sich der Band-
wurm in der Darmwand
des Wirtes (Nagetiere,
Mensch) verankert.
Fixation mit Glutaralde-
hyd, Trocknung am kriti-
schen Punkt mit Freon,
Bedampfung mit C + Au.
*(H.P. Schulz, R. Holm,
Bayer AG)*

Fig. 110. Scolex of the
tapeworm Hymenolepis
nana with four suckers
and the circle of hooks
on the protruded rostel-
lum. The suckers and
hooks are used by the
tapeworm to attach itself
to the intestinal wall of
the host (rodent or man).
Fixation with glutaralde-
hyde, critical point
drying with Freon, C + Au
vapor-coated.

Abb. 111. Hakenkranz
am ausgestülpten Ro-
stellum des *Bandwurms*.
*(H.P. Schulz, R. Holm,
Bayer AG)*

Fig. 111. Hook crown on
the protruded rostel-
lum of the *tapeworm*.

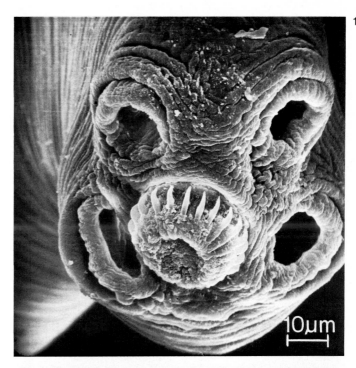

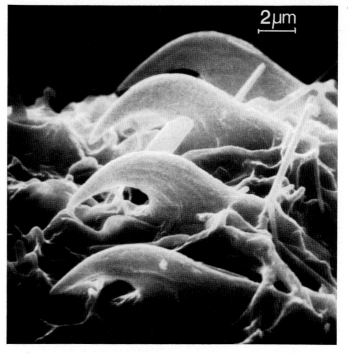

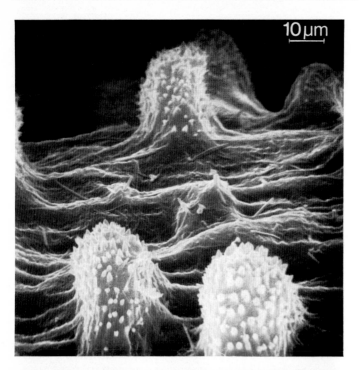

10 µm

Abb. 112. Warzenförmige Hautfalten des *Pärchen-egels* (Schistosoma man-soni), die der Haftung am Blutgefäß dienen.
(*H.P. Schulz, R. Holm,* Bayer AG)

Fig. 112. Spiked "warts" of *Schistosoma mansoni,* which facilitate fixation in the blood vessel.

50 µm

Abb. 113. *Pärchenengel* (Schistosoma mansoni). In der Hautfalte des männlichen Tieres ist das wesentlich dünnere weib-liche Tier teilweise ver-borgen. Gefriergetrock-net, C-Au-bedampft.
(*H.P. Schulz, R. Holm,* Bayer AG)

Fig. 113. *Schistosoma mansoni.* The female is lying in a pouch of the much larger male. Freeze-dried, C-Au-coated.

Abb. 114. *Bandwurm* (Taenia taeniaeformis). Kopfpartie mit vier Saugnäpfen und teilweise ausgestülptem Rostellum mit doppelten Hakenkranz. Einzelne Haken wurden bei der Präparation gelöst. Gefriertrocknung, Cu-Au-bedampft. (*H.P. Schulz, R. Holm,* Bayer AG)

Fig. 114. *Tapeworm* (Taenia taeniaeformis). Head with four suckers and partially protruded rostellum with double hook crown. Individual hooks were loosened during the preparation. Freeze-dried, C-Au-coated.

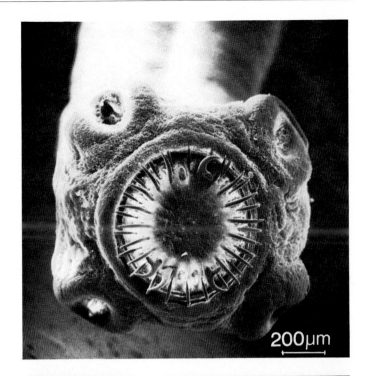

Abb. 115. Hakenkranz aus Abb. 114. (*H.P. Schulz, R. Holm,* Bayer AG)

Fig. 115. *Hook crown* from Fig. 114.

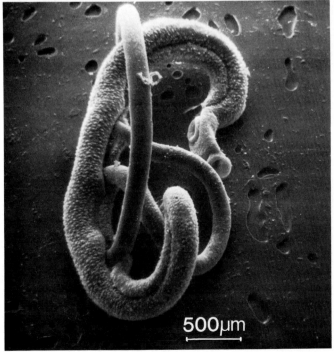

Abb. 116. *Fliegenkopf.*
Antennen mit Arista und
Pedicellus. Komplexau-
gen und drei Ocellen.
C-Au-bedampft.
(G. Heyl, R. Holm,
Bayer AG)

Fig. 116. *Head of a fly.*
Antennae with arista and
pedicellus, complex eyes
and three ocellae. C-Au-
coated.

200µm

Abb. 117. Komplexauge
des Fliegenkopfes. Om-
matidium mit Trichome.
(G. Heyl, R. Holm,
Bayer AG)

Fig. 117. *Complex eye*
of a fly. Ommatidium with
trichome.

20µm

Abb. 118. *Fliege* Musca autumnalis (De Geer).
a) Caput und vorderer Thoraxteil von latero-ventral. Es sind u.a. ein Facettenauge, der Rüssel, die Antennen und die proximalen Glieder des ersten Beinpaares sichtbar
b) Aufsicht auf den Saug-rüssel, neben der Saugscheibe ein Maxillartaster sichtbar.
Fixation in Glutaraldehyd, Trocknung am kritischen Punkt, Bedampfung mit C + Au. (*W. Stendel, R. Holm,* Bayer AG)

Fig. 118. Fly Musca au-tumnalis (De Geer).
a) Lateroventral surface of head and anterior part of thorax: one eye, the proboscis, anten-nae and proximal seg-ments of the first pair of legs;
b) Distal end of the pro-boscis everted to form a sucking disk, next to it a maxillary palp.
Fixation in glutaraldehyde, drying at the critical point, C + Au vapor-coated.

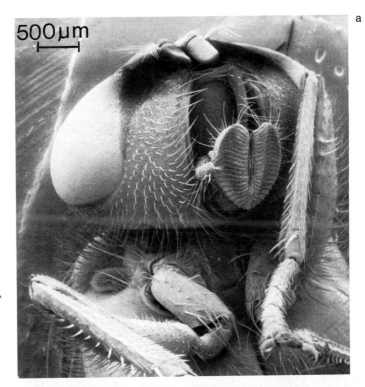

Abb. 119. *Anopheles-mücke,* weiblich, Gesamt-habitus mit Facetten-augen, Fühlern, Stechrüssel und Palpen. C-Au-bedampft.
(*H.P. Schulz, R. Holm,* Bayer AG)

Fig. 119. *Anopheles mosquito,* female, overall view with facet eyes. antennae, proboscis and palps. C-Au-coated.

Abb. 120. Kopf der *Anophelesmücke,* Seiten-ansicht. (*H.P. Schulz, R. Holm,* Bayer AG)

Fig. 120. Head of a female *Anopheles mos-quito,* lateral view.

Abb. 121. Kopf der *Gelbfiebermücke* (Aëdes aegypti) mit Komplexaugen, Antennen, Stechrüssel und Palpen. Lufttrocknung. C-Au-bedampft. (*H.P. Schulz, R. Holm,* Bayer AG)

Fig. 121. *Head of a yellow-fever mosquito* (Aëdes aegypti) with complex eyes, antennae, proboscis and palps. Air-dried, C-Au-coated.

Abb. 122. *Ameisenkopf* mit Fühlern und dahinter-liegenden Komplexaugen. C-Au-bedampft. (*L. Morbitzer*, Bayer AG)

Fig. 122. *Head of an ant* with antennae and complex eyes behind them. C-Au-coated.

Abb. 123. Ameisenkopf, Mandibeln mit Sinnes-haaren. C-Au-bedampft. (*L. Morbitzer*, Bayer AG)

Fig. 123. *Head of an ant,* mandibles with sense hairs, C-Au-coated.

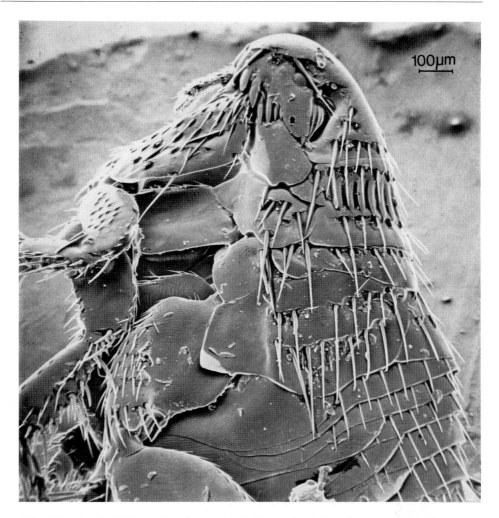

Abb. 124. *Hundfloh* (Ctenocéphalus canis). Luftgetrocknet, C-Au-bedampft. (*M. Pfautsch,* München)

Fig. 124. *Dog flea* (Ctenocephalus canis), air-dried, C-Au-coated.

125 a

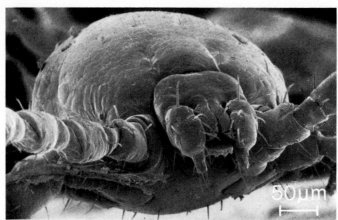

125 b

125 c

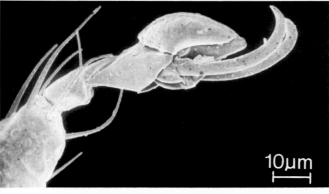

Abb. 125. Mund- und Haftwerkzeuge von *Zecken*.
a) Boophilus decoloratus (Larve), Gesamtansicht von kraniodorsal,
b) Boophilus decoloratus (Larve) mit Zähnchen besetztes Hypostom von ventral,
c) Boophilus microplus, Klaue mit Krallen und Haftscheibe (Pulvillus) von lateral.
Fixation in Glutaraldehyd, Lufttrocknung, Bedampfung mit C + Au. (*W. Stendel, R. Holm,* Bayer AG)

Fig. 125. Mouth parts and attachment organs of *ticks*.
a) Boophilus decoloratus (larva), craniodorsal view;
b) Boophilus decoloratus (larva), ventral aspect of hypostome with longitudinal rows of dentides;
c) Boophilus microplus (larva), lateral view of claws and pad (pulvillus).
Fixation in glutaraldehyde, air drying, A + Au vaporcoated.

Abb. 126. Schrilleisten auf der Flügeldecke eines Käfers. Luftgetrocknet, ohne Fixation, C-Au-C-bedampft. (*H.G. Fromme,* Münster)

Fig. 126. Scutellum of a *beetle*. The *files* and *ridges*, with which the animal produce sound. Air-dried, without fixation, C-Au-C-coated.

Abb. 127. Vogelfeder mit Radii, Radioli und Häkchen. C-Au-bedampft. (*G. Heyl,* Bayer AG)

Fig. 127. *Bird feather* with radii, radioli and hooks, C-Au-coated.

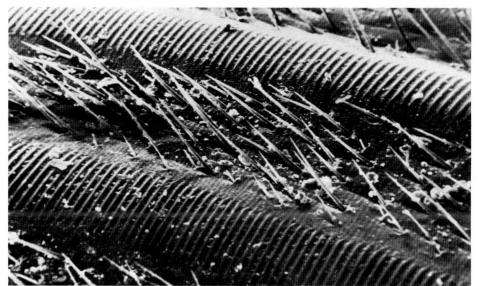

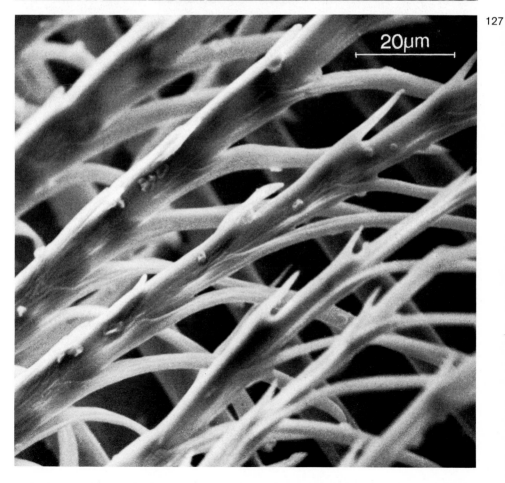

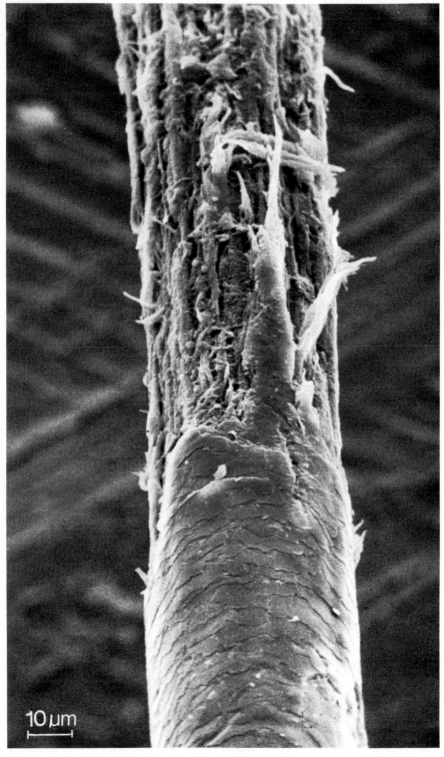

10 µm

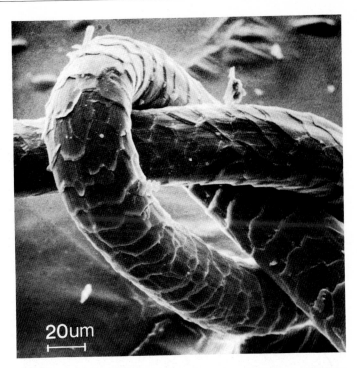

Abb. 129. *Wollfaser* (Schaf) verknotet, mit charakteristischer Kutikulastruktur. C-Au-bedampft.

Fig. 129. *Wool fibre* (sheep) knotted, with characteristic cuticular structure. C-Au-coated.

◁ Abb. 128. *Menschliches Kopfhaar* bei Pilzbefall (Trichophyton Schoenleinii). Im oberen Haaranteil ist die Kutikula geschädigt und der Kortex freigelegt. Glutaraldehydfixation, Azeton-Entwässerung. C-Au-bedampft. (*C. Orfanos, G. Mahrle, M. Piroth,* Köln)

Fig. 128. *Human head hair* with fungus infection (Trichophyton Schoenleinii). In the upper part of the hair the cuticula is damaged and the cortex becomes visible. Glutaraldehyde fixation, dehydration with acetone, C-Au-coated.

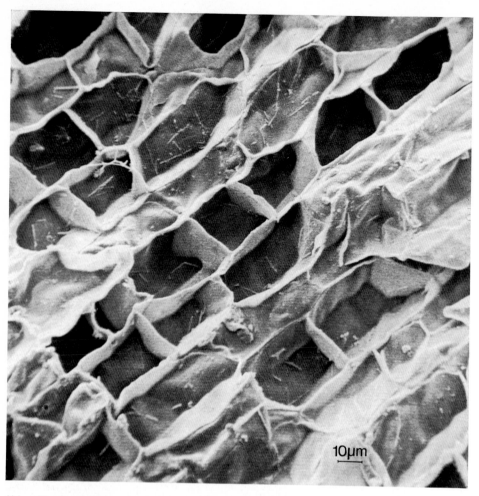

Abb. 130. Bruchfläche eines *Flaschenkorkens.* C-Au-bedampft. (*M. Bode,* Münster)

Fig. 130. Fracture surface of a *bottle cork.* C-Au-coated.

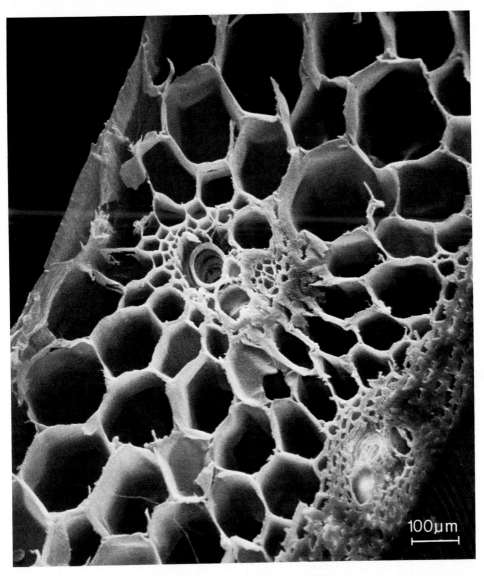

Abb. 131. Querschnitt durch die Wand eines *Strohhalmes*. C-Au-bedampft. (*B. Böhlken, H. Klingele*, München)

Fig. 131. Section through the wall of a *straw*. C + Au vapor-coated.

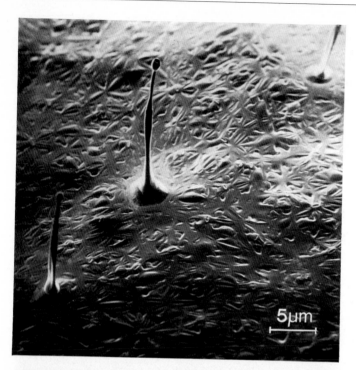

Abb. 132. *Tabakblatt,*
Oberseite mit Drüsen-
haaren, C-Au-bedampft.
(*G. Heyl,* Bayer AG)

Fig. 132. *Tobacco leaf,*
surface with gland hairs,
C-Au-coated.

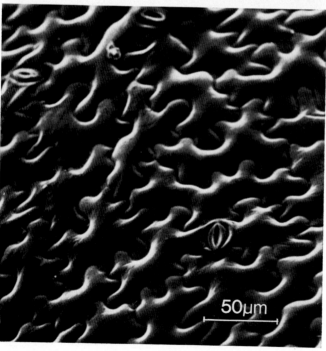

Abb. 133. *Salatblatt.*
Einzelne Spaltöffnungen
zwischen den verzahnten
Epidermiszellen; unbe-
dampft, Primärstrahl-
spannung 10 kV.
(*G. Heyl,* Bayer AG)

Fig. 133. *Lettuce leaf.*
Some stomata between
the epidermal cells.
Uncoated, primary
electron beam 10 kV.

Abb. 134. Einzellige *Grünalge* Acetabularia major.
a) Hut der Grünalge,
b) Rhizoid der Grünalge.
Fixation mit Glutaraldehyd und OsO_4, Trocknung am kritischen Punkt mit Freon, Bedampfung mit C + Au. (*S. BERGER*, Wilhelmshaven; *G. LANGE*, Leverkusen)

Fig. 134. Monocellular *green alga* Acetabularia major.
a) young cap,
b) rhizoid.
Fixation with glutaraldehyde and OsO_4, critical point drying with Freon, C + Au vapor-coated.

400μm   a

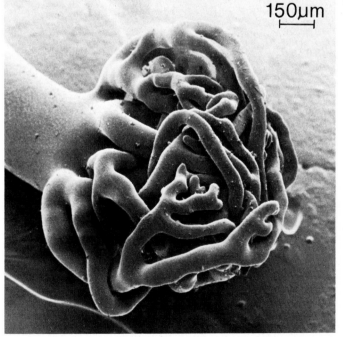

150μm   b

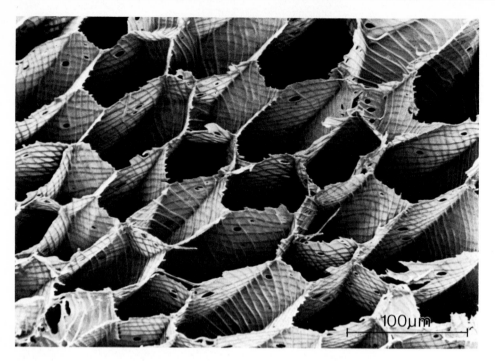

Abb. 135. Schrägschnitt durch die Rhizodermis (Velamen radicum) einer Luftwurzel der *Orchidee* (Dendrobium superbum Reichb. f.). Die toten luftgefüllten Zellen sind durch leistenartige Wandverdickungen verstärkt, die mit der Funktion der Wasseraufnahme des Gewebes zusammenhängen.
Lufttrocken, Au-besputtered in Argon-Atmosphäre. (*W. Barthlott,* Heidelberg)

Fig. 135. Oblique section through the rhizodermis (velamen radicum) of an aerial root of the *orchid* (Dendrobium superbum Reichb. f.). The dead air-filled cells are reinforced by secondary wall thickenings, which are related to the water-absorbing function of the tissue.
Air-dried, Au sputter-coated.

Abb. 136. Spitze eines *Glochiden-Stachels* von Opuntia microdasys (*Lehm) Pfeiff.* (Cacta- ▷ ceae) mit schräg umgekippten Papillenzellen der Epidermis, die dem feinen Dorn eine Widerhakenfunktion verleihen.
Lufttrocken, Au-besputtered in Argon-Atmosphäre. (*W. Barthlott, N. Ehler,* Heidelberg)

Fig. 136. Tip of a *glochid spine* of Opuntia microdasys *(Lehm.) Pfeiff.* (Cactaceae) with obliquely turned-back papillary cells of the epidermis, which make the delicate thorn similar to a barb.
Air-dried, Au sputter coated.

Abb. 137. *Kakteenstachel* (Ferocactus emoryi [Eng.] Backebg.) mit lang papillenartig ausge- ▷ zogenen Zellen der Dornepidermis.
Lufttrocken, C-Au-bedampft. (*W. Barthlott, N. Ehler, R. Schill,* Heidelberg)

Fig. 137. *Cactus spine* (Ferocactus emoryi [Eng.] Backebg.) with long drawn-out papilla-like cells of the epidermis.
Air-dried, C + Au vapor-coated.

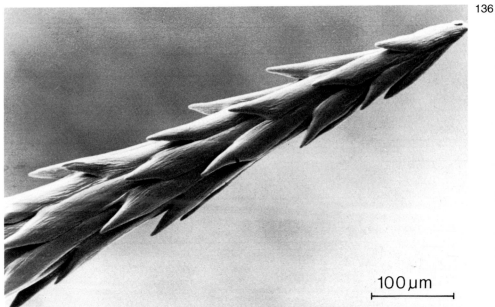

136

100 µm

137

10 µm

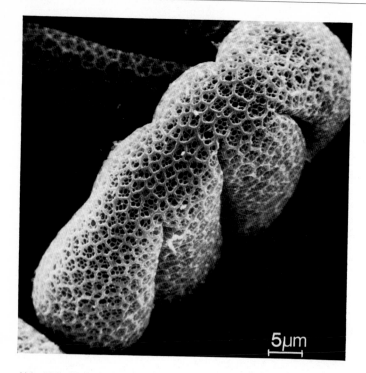

Abb. 138. *Pollen* (Salvia splendus). Luftgetrocknet, C-Au-bedampft. (*G. Heyl, R. Holm,* Bayer AG)

Fig. 138. *Pollen* (Salvia splendus) air-dried, C-Au-coated.

Abb. 139. Blütenbatt der *Hundskamille* (Anthemis tinctoria L. ▷ [Asteraceae]) mit papillösen Epidermiszellen, die durch ein feines regelmäßiges Faltenmuster der Cuticula skulpturiert sind. Rechts im Bild ein Pollenkorn von Anthemis.
C-Au-bedampft. (*W. Barthlott, N. Ehler,* Heidelberg)

Fig. 139. Flower petal of Anthemis tinctoria L. (Asteraceae) with epidermal papillae sculptured by the fine and regular cuticular fold pattern. A pollen grain is seen at the right of the picture.
C + Au vapor-coated.

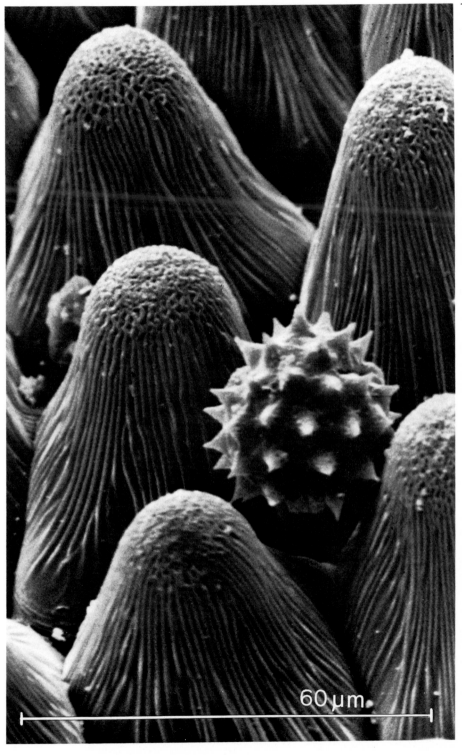

60 µm

Abb. 140. Pilzsporen von Laccaria laccata (Scop. ex. Fr.) Bk. u. Br. (rötlicher Lacktrichterling). Gefriergetrocknet, C-Au-bedampft. (*H. Wollweber, R. Holm,* Bayer AG)

Fig. 140. *Fungus spores* of Laccaria laccata (Scop. ex. Fr.) Bk. et Br. Freezedried, C-Au-coated.

Abb. 141. Pilzsporen von Inocybe asterospora Quél (sternsporiger Rißpilz). Gefriergetrocknet, C-Au-bedampft. (*H. Wollweber, R. Holm,* Bayer AG)

Fig. 141. *Fungus spores* of Inocybe asterospora Quél. Freeze-dried, C-Au-coated.

Abb. 142. Pilzsporen von
Coprinus micaceus,
Übersichtsaufnahme.
Glutaraldehydfixation,
nach der kritischen Punkt-
Methode getrocknet mit
Freon 13.
(*H. Wollweber,*
R. Holm, Bayer AG)

Fig. 142. *Fungus spores*
of Coprinus micaceus.
Glutaraldehyde fixation,
prepared by the critical
drying method with freon
13, C-Au-coated.

Abb. 143. Pilzsporen von
Coprinus micaceus (Bull
ex. Fr.). Fr. (Glimmertin-
ling). Basidien mit Sporen.
Glutaraldehydfixierung,
nach der kritischen
Punkt-Methode gtrocknet
mit Freon 13, C-Au-be-
dampft. (*H. Wollweber,*
R. Holm, Bayer AG)

Fig. 143. *Fungus spores*
of Coprinus micaceus
(Bull. ex. Fr.) Fr. Basidia
with spores. Glutaralde-
hyde fixation, prepared by
the critical point drying
method with Freon 13,
C-Au-coated.

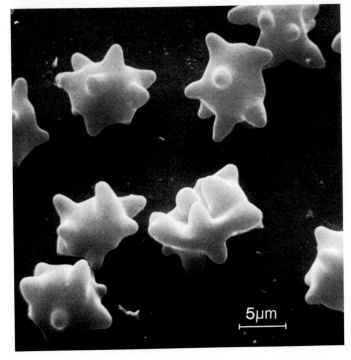

Literatur

Das nachfolgende Literaturverzeichnis erhebt keinen Anspruch auf Vollständigkeit, sondern soll dem interessierten Leser lediglich eine *Orientierungshilfe* bieten.
Wer die ständig steigende Zahl der rasterelektronenmikroskopischen Veröffentlichungen verfolgen möchte, sei auf die *Literatursammlungen* hingewiesen, die zusammengestellt werden von:

Pfefferkorn, G., und Ehrenwerth, U., Institut für medizinische Physik der Universität Münster, 44 Münster, Hüfferstr. 68 (Deutschland)

Wells, O. C., IBM, Thomas J. Watson Research Center, Post Office Box 218, Yorktown Heights, New York 10 598 (USA)

Die wichtigsten neuen Erkenntnisse auf dem Gebiet der Rasterelektronenmikroskopie werden zur Zeit überwiegend in den folgenden, jährlich erscheinenden *Sammelbänden* veröffentlicht:

Beitr. elektronenmikroskop. Direktabb. Oberfl. (BEDO). Herausgeber Prof. Dr. G. Pfefferkorn, 44 Münster, Hüfferstr. 68 (Deutschland)

Scanning Electron Microscopy, Proceedings of the Annual Scanning Electron Microscope Symposium, Direktor und Herausgeber Dr. Om Johari, P.O. Box 66 507, AMF O'HARE, IL 60 666, USA (früher: IIT Research Institute [IITRI] Chicago, Illinois 60 616 [USA])

Literature

The following list of literature is by no means complete. It is intended to serve the reader only as a *guide.*
Those who wish to follow the steadily increasing stream of papers on scanning electron microscopy are advised of *collections of current literature,* which are being made by:

Pfefferkorn, G., and Ehrenwerth, U., Institute of Medical Physics, University of Münster, 44 Münster, Hüfferstr. 68 (Germany)

Wells, O. C., IBM, Thomas J. Watson Research Center, P.O. Box 218, Yorktown Heights, New York 10 598 (USA)

The more important new results in scanning electron microscopy are at present published in the following *annual volumes:*

Beitr. elektronenmikroskop. Direktabb. Oberfl. (BEDO). Editor Prof. Dr. G. Pfefferkorn, 44 Münster, Hüfferstr. 68 (Germany)

Scanning Electron Microscopy, Proceedings of the Annual Scanning Electron Microscope Symposium, Director and Editor Dr. Om Johari, P.O. Box 66 507, AMF O'HARE, IL 60 666, USA (formerly: IIT Research Institute [IITRI], Chicago, Illinois 60 616 [USA])

Die folgende Literatur ist eingeteilt in:

1. Allgemeine Arbeiten, Monographien und Bibliographien zur Rasterelektronenmikroskopie
2. Arbeiten zur Technik des Rasterelektronenmikroskops
3. Arbeiten zur Präparationstechnik
4. Rasterelektronenmikroskopische Arbeiten zu einzelnen Objekten
5. Sonstige Arbeiten aus angrenzenden Fachgebieten

The following literature is divided into:

1. General papers, monographs, and bibliographies on scanning electron microscopy
2. Technical papers on the scanning electron microscope
3. Papers on preparation techniques
4. Papers on scanning electron microscopic studies of individual specimens
5. Other papers from adjoining fields

1. Allgemeine Arbeiten, Monographien und Bibliographien zur Rasterelektronenmikroskopie

General papers, monographs, and bibliographies on scanning electron microscopy

Böhm, E.: Die Anwendung des Rasterelektronenmikroskops in der Rechtsmedizin. Beitr. gerichtl. Med. 28 (1971) 121

Boyde, A.: A review of problems of interpretation of the scanning electron microscope image with special regard to methods of specimen preparation. Scanning Electron Microscopy, IITRI, Chicago (1971) 3–8

Boyde, A., S. J. Jones, E. Bailey: Biomedical applications of SEM. Scanning Electron Microscopy, IITRI, Chicago (1972) 697

Bröcker, W., G. Pfefferkorn: Bibliographie über Kathodolumineszenz. Beitr. elektronenmikroskop. Direktabb. Oberfl. (BEDO) Münster (1975) 143

Bröcker, W., G. Pfefferkorn: Bibliography on cathodoluminescence. Scanning Electron Microscopy, IITRI, Chicago (1976) 725–736

Cosslett, V. E.: Modern Microscopy. Bell, London 1966

Echlin, P.: Application of SEM and X-ray microanalysis in the plant sciences. Scanning Electron Microscopy, IITRI, Chicago (1974) 477

Echlin, P., M. Gregory: Application of SEM and X-ray microanalysis in the plant sciences. Scanning Electron Microscopy, IITRI, Chicago (1975) 737

Fromme, H. G., M. Pfautsch: Bibliographie zur Methodik und Anwendung der „Kritischen-Punkt-Trocknung". Beitr. elektronenmikroskop. Direktabb. Oberfl. (BEDO) Münster (1975) 123

Fujita, T., M. D. J. Tokunaga, H. Inoue: Atlas of Scanning Electron Microscopy in Medicine. Igaku Shoin, Tokyo 1971

Hayes, T. L., R. F. W. Pease: The scanning electron microscope: principles and applications in biology and medicine. Advanc. biol. med. Phys. 12 (1968) 85

Hearle, J. W. S., J. T. Sparrow, P. M. Cross: The Use of Scanning Electron Microscope. Pergamon Press, New York 1972

Heyl, G., R. Holm, J. Ohnsorge: Möglichkeiten der Rasterelektronenmikroskopie. Ther. Ber. (Bayer) 42 (1970) 127–132

Heywood, V. H.: Scanning Electron Microscopy. Systematic and Evolutionary Applications. Academic Press, London 1971

Holm, R.: Neuere Entwicklungen in der Rasterelektronenmikroskopie. G-I-T-Fachz. Lab. 17 (1973) 315–326/453–459

Holt, D. B., M. D. Muir, P. R. Grant, I. M. Boswarva: Quantitative Scanning Electron Microscopy. Academic Press, London 1974

Johari, O.: Umfassende Material-Charakterisierung mit dem Raster-Elektronenmikroskop. Microsc. Acta 75 (1973) 1–19

Johnson, V. E.: SEM in material sciences. Scanning Electron Microscopy, IITRI, Chicago (1975) 763

Jones, S. C., E. Bailey, A. Boyde: Biomedical applications. Scanning Electron Microscopy, IITRI, Chicago (1974) 835

Kessel, R. G., C. Y. Shih: Scanning Electron Microscopy in Biology – A Students' Atlas on Biological Organization. Springer, Berlin 1974

McMullan, D.: The scanning electron microscope and the electron-optical examination of surfaces. Electronic Engng. 25 (1953) 46–50

Nixon, W. C.: Scanning electron microscopy. J. roy. micr. Soc. 83 (1964) 213–216

Oatley, C. W.: The scanning electron microscope. New Scientist 12 (1958) 153–155

Oatley, C. W.: The Scanning Electron Microscope, part I: The Instrument. Cambridge University Press, London 1972

Oatley, C. W., W. C. Nixon, R. F. W. Pease: Scanning electron microscopy. Advanc. Electronics Electron Phys. 21 (1965) 181–247

Pease, R. F. W.: High resolution scanning electron microscopy. Diss., Cambridge 1963

Pease, R. F. W., T. L. Hayes, A. S. Camp, N. M. Amer: Electron microscopy of living insects. Science 154 (1966) 1185–1186

Pfefferkorn, G.: Rückblick auf die Entwicklung der elektronenmikroskopischen Direktabbildung von Oberflächen. Beitr. elektronenmikroskop. Direktabb. Oberfl. 3 (1970) 1–16

Pfefferkorn, G.: A bibliography on fundamentals of SEM for biologists. Scanning Electron Microscopy, IITRI/Chicago (1977) 569–570

Pfefferkorn, G., R. Blaschke: Raster-Elektronenmikroskop für Oberflächenuntersuchungen. Umschau, Frankfurt 1967 (S. 584–590)

Pfefferkorn, G., R. Blaschke: Der Informationsgehalt rasterelektronenmikroskopischer Aufnahmen. Beitr. elektronenmikroskop. Direktabb. Oberfl. 1 (1968) 1–26

Polke, M.: Raster-Elektronenmikroskopie an Festkörperoberflächen. G-I-T, Fachz. Lab. 12, H. 9 (1968) 873–879

Reimer, L., G. Pfefferkorn: Raster-Elektronenmikroskopie. Springer, Berlin 1977

Reumuth, H.: Die Raster-Elektronenmikroskopie. Dtsch. med. Wschr. 94 (1969) 1832–1837

Seiler, A.: Abbildung von Oberflächen mit Elektronen, Ionen und Röntgenstrahlen. B. I. Hochschultaschenbücher Bd. 428/428 a. Bibliographisches Institut, Mannheim 1968

Smith, K. C. A., C. W. Oatley: The scanning electron microscopy and its fields of application. Brit. J. appl. Phys. 6 (1955) 391–399

Stewart, W. D.: Bibliography on forensic applications of the SEM. Scanning Electron Microscopy, IITRI, Chicago (1976) 739–743

Thornton, P. R.: Scanning Electron Microscopy. Applications to Materials and Device Science. Chapman & Hall, London 1968

Wells, O. C.: The Construction of a Scanning Electron Microscope and its Application to the Study of Fibres. Diss., Cambridge 1957

Wells, O. C.: Scanning Electron Microscopy. McGraw-Hill, New York 1974

Yoshii, Z., J. Tokunaga, J. Tawara: Atlas of Scanning Electron Microscopy in Microbiology. Thieme, Stuttgart 1976

Zworykin, V. K., G. A. Morton, E. G. Ramberg, A. W. Vance: Electron Optics and Electron Microscope. Wiley, New York 1945

2. Arbeiten zur Technik des Rasterelektronenmikroskops
Technical papers on the scanning electron microscope

von Ardenne, M.: Das Elektronenmikroskop. Theoretische Grundlagen. Z. Phys. 109 (1938) 553–572

von Ardenne, M.: Das Elektronen-Raster-Mikroskop. Z. Techn. Phys. 19 (1938) 407–416

Ayres, A., J. M. Allen, A. E. Williams: A method for obtaining conventional histological sections from specimens after examination by scanning electron microscopy. J. Microsc. (Oxf.) 93 (1971) 247–250

Balk, L. J., E. Kubalek: Micron scaled cathodoluminescence of semiconductors. Scanning Electron Microscopy, IITRI, Chicago (1977) 739

von Bassewitz, K., R. Holm: REM-Untersuchungen an schlagzähem Polystyrol: Direkte Beobachtung der Festigkeit gegenüber Zugbeanspruchung und des Craze-Wachstums. Beitr. elektronenmikroskop. Direktabb. Oberfl. 5 (1972) 763–776

Blaschke, R.: Materialanalyse mit dem Raster-Elektronenmikroskop, dem Photoemissions-Elektronenmikroskop und dem Elektronenstrahl-Röntgenmikroanalysator. Beitr. elektronenmikroskop. Direktabb. Oberfl. 3 (1970) 17–36

Blaschke, R.: Ein Präparathalter für Durchstrahlungsexperimente und für Stereobildpaare. Beitr. elektronenmikroskop. Direktabb. Oberfl. 3 (1970) 161–166

Blaschke, R., K. Fecher: Ein einfacher Präparathalter für Objektwendungen und für Stereoaufnahmen. Beitr. elektronenmikroskop. Direktabb. Oberfl. 1 (1968) 305–308

Boyde, A.: Height measurements from stereopair scanning electron micrographs. Beitr. elektronenmikroskop. Direktabb. Oberfl. 1 (1968) 97–106

Boyde, A., P. G. Howell, S. J. Jones: Measurement of lacunar volume in bone using a stereological grid counting method evolved for the scanning electron microscope. J. Microsc. (Oxf.) 101 (1974) 261–266

Brandis, E. K., R. Holm: Vorteile und Probleme bei der Auger-Mikroanalyse im Rasterelektronenmikroskop. Beitr. elektronenmikroskop. Direktabb. Oberfl. 8 (1975) 89–104

Bröcker, W.: Biologisch-medizinische Anwendungen der Kathodolumineszenz. Beitr. elektronenmikroskop. Direktabb. Oberfl. (BEDO) 8 (1975) 187–202

Bröcker, W., E. H. Schmidt, G. Pfefferkorn, F. K. Beller: Demonstration of cathodoluminescence in fluorescein marked biological tissues. Scanning Electron Microscopy, IITRI, Chicago (1975) 243 bis 250

Broers, A. N.: Factors affecting resolution in the SEM. Scanning Electron Microscopy, IITRI, Chicago (1970) 3–8

Broers, A. N., B. J. Panessa, J. F. Gennaro: High resolution SEM of biological specimens. Scanning Electron Microscopy, IITRI, Chicago (1975) 233 bis 242

Brown, A. C., J. A. Swift: Rasterelektronenmikroskopie von geschnittenem biologischen Material mit dem Element-Kontrastverfahren. Beitr. elektronenmikroskop. Direktabb. Oberfl. 3 (1970) 299–306

Ceccarelli, B., F. Clementi, C. de Cuili, D. Marini: Note techniche per l'applicazione in biologiadel microscopio elettronico a scansione. Boll. Soc. ital. Biol. sper. 45 (1969) 644–646

Christenhuß, R., G. Pfefferkorn: Bild-Drehung und -Verzerrung beim Raster-Elektronenmikroskop Stereoscan. Beitr. elektronenmikroskop. Direktabb. Oberfl. 1 (1968) 129–140

Christou, A.: Correlation of low loss electron images with auger images of semiconductor substrate surfaces. Scanning Electron Microscopy, IITRI, Chicago (1977) 159–166

Corvin, I., O. Johari: Influence of topography on contrast of SEM images. VII. Congr. Intern. Microscopie électronique, Grenoble 1 (1970) 219

Crewe, A. V.: High resolution scanning microscopy of biological specimens. Ber. Bunsenges. 74 (1970) 1181–1187

Crewe, A. V., M. Isaacson: Secondary electron detection in a field emission scanning microscope. Rev. Sci. Instrum. 41 (1970) 20–24

Crewe, A. V., J. Wall: Contrast in a high resolution scanning transmission electron microscope. Optik 30 (1970) 461–474

Crewe, A. V., J. Wall, J. Langmore: Single atom visibility. VII. Congr. Intern. Microscopie électronique, Grenoble 1 (1970) 485

Davey, J. P.: Electron microprobe scanning system for the study of luminescence. Diss., Cambridge 1965

Dingley, D. J.: A simple straining stage for the scanning electron microscope. Micron 1 (1969) 206–210

Everhart, T. E., O. C. Wells, C. W. Oatley: Factors affecting contrast and resolution in the scanning electron microscope. J. Electronics and Control 7 (1959) 97–111

Freund, F., R. Holm: Beobachtungen bei der Oxidation von Wolfram im REM. Beitr. elektronenmikroskop. Direktabb. Oberfl. (BEDO) 8 (1975) 593–596

Hamza, A. A.: The present state of development of dynamic experiments in the specimen chamber of the scanning electron microscope. Scanning Electron Microscopy, IITRI, Chicago (1977) 703

Hantsche, H.: Zur quantitativen Röntgenmikroanalyse. Beitr. elektronenmikroskop. Direktabb. Oberfl. (BEDO) 7 (1974) 531–555

Helmcke, J.-G.: Abbildung nichtleitender organischer Strukturen. Probleme der Kontrastentstehung und der Stereoskopie am Raster-Elektronenmikroskop. Beitr. elektronenmikroskop. Direktabb. Oberfl. 2 (1969) 207–212

Heyl, G., R. Holm: Kathodolumineszenz - eine Art

Fluoreszenzmikroskopie mit der Schärfentiefe des Rasterelektronenmikroskops. Beitr. elektronenmikroskop. Direktabb. Oberfl. 3 (1970) 193–202

Herbst, R., A.-M. Multier: Die Elektronenstrahlmikroanalyse biologischer Weichgewebe. Verh. dtsch. path. Ges. 54 (1970) 578

Höhling, H. J., E. R. Krefting, W. A. P. Nicholson: Anwendung der Elektronenstrahlmikroanalyse in der Hartgewebsforschung. Beitr. elektronenmikroskop. Direktabb. Oberfl. (BEDO) 8 (1975) 125–146

Hörl, E. M.: Verbessertes Ellipsenspiegel-Detektorsystem für die Kathodolumineszenz-Rasterelektronenmikroskopie. Beitr. elektronenmikroskop. Direktabb. Oberfl. (BEDO) 8 (1975) 369–374

Hörl, E. M., F. Buschbeck: Rasterelektronenmikroskopie unter Verwendung eines Farbmonitors. Beitr. elektronenmikroskop. Direktabb. Oberfl. (BEDO) 8 (1975) 233–244

Hörl, E. M., E. Mügschl: Rasterelektronenmikroskopie mit Hilfe der Lilienfeldstrahlung. Beitr. elektronenmikroskop. Direktabb. Oberfl. (BEDO) 5 (1972) 313–321

Holm, R.: Abbildung und Analyse von Oberflächen mit Rasterelektronenmikroskop und Elektronenspektrometer. Angew. Chem. 83 (1971) 632–645

Holm, R.: Imaging and analysis of surfaces with a scanning electron microscope and electron spectrometer. Angew. Chem. Int. Ed. 10 (1971) 591–598

Holm, R.: Dynamische Experimente im Rasterelektronenmikroskop. Beitr. elektronenmikroskop. Direktabb. Oberfl. 5 (1972) 347–352

Holm, R., L. Morbitzer: Dehnungs- und Bruchexperimente an glasfaserverstärkten Thermoplasten. Beitr. elektronenmikroskop. Direktabb. Oberfl. 5 (1972) 777–780

Holm, R., L. Morbitzer: Dynamic experiments with a hot stage in the SEM. Beitr. elektronenmikroskop. Direktabb. Oberfl. (BEDO) 6 (1973) 177–180

Holm, R., B. Reinfandt: Dynamische Experimente im REM unter Verwendung spezieller Probenbühnen. Feinwerktechnik u. Meßtechnik 83 (1975) 126–130

Kato, Y., S. Fukuhara, T. Komoda: Steroscopic observation and three-dimensional measurement for scanning electron microscopy. Scanning Electron Microscopy, IITRI, Chicago (1977) 41–48

Kimoto, S., H. Hashimoto: Stereoscopic observation in scanning microscopy using multiple detectors. In: The Electron Microprobe, Proc. Symposium, Washington 1964, hrsg. von McKinley u. a. Wiley, New York 1966 (S. 480–489)

Knoll, M.: Aufladepotential und Sekundäremission elektronenbestrahlter Oberflächen. Z. Techn. Phys. 2 (1935) 467

Knoll, M.: Steuerwirkung eines geladenen Teilchens im Feld einer Sekundäremissionskathode. Naturwissenschaften 29 (1941) 335–336

Knoll, M., E. Theile: Elektronenabtaster zur Strukturabbildung von Oberflächen und dünnen Schichten. Z. Phys. 113 (1939) 260–280

Krisch, B., K.-H. Müller, M. v. Rauch, R. Schliepe, H. M. Thieringer: Analytical microscopy using a high resolution STEM. Scanning Electron Microscopy, IITRI, Chicago (1977) 423–430

Lindemann, B., W. Fuchs, J. D. Brombach: Nachweis diffusibler Ionen in biologischen Präparaten mit-

tels energiedispersiver Elektronenstrahlmikroanalyse. Beitr. elektronenmikroskop. Direktabb. Oberfl. (BEDO) 8 (1975) 147

MacDonald, N. C., C. T. Hovland, R. L. Gerlach: Scanning auger microscopy for microelectronic device characterization and quality control. Scanning Electron Microscopy, IITRI, Chicago (1977) 201–210

Manger, W. M., M. Bessis: Cathodoluminescence produced in cells and proteins by paraformaldehyde as seen with the scanning electron microscope. VII. Congr. Intern. Microscopie électronique, Grenoble (1970) 483

Norton, J. F., G. E. Possin, C. G. Kirkpatrick: Movable faraday cup, illuminator and backscattering diode detectors for SEM. Scanning Electron Microscopy, IITRI, Chicago (1977) 155–158

Oatley, C. W.: New electron-probe instruments. Electronics and Power 12 (1966) 282–285

Ohnsorge, J.: Festkörperoberflächenuntersuchungen mit Hilfe des Rasterelektronenmikroskops. Z. Orthop. 107 (1970) 213–220

Ohnsorge, J.: Möglichkeiten und Grenzen der Rasterelektronenmikroskopie. Beitr. gericht. Med. 29 (1972) 259–265

Ohnsorge, J., R. Holm: Materialanalyse im Rasterelektronenmikroskop. Scr. med. Fac. Med. Brun. 47 (1974) 143–149

Orloff, J., L. W. Swanson: A scanning ion microscope with a field ionization source. Scanning Electron Microscopy, IITRI, Chicago (1977) 57–62

Reimer, L.: Electron-specimen interactions and applications in SEM and STEM. Scanning Electron Microscopy, IITRI, Chicago (1976) 1–8

Reimer, L., T. Rieke, G. Tüllmann: Abbildung mit Rückstreu- und Sekundärelektronen in einem Transmissionselektronenmikroskop mit Rasterzusatz. Beitr. elektronenmikroskop. Direktabb. Oberfl. (BEDO) 8 (1975) 775–792

Reumuth, H.: Leistungs- und Prinzip-Vergleiche zwischen Lichtmikroskopen, Durchstrahlungs-Elektronenmikroskopen und dem neuen Raster-Aufstrahlungs-Elektronenmikroskop Stereoscan 1966. Melliand Textilber. 48 (1967) 489–501

Russ, J. C.: Selecting optimum KV for STEM microanalysis. Scanning Electron Microscopy, IITRI, Chicago (1977) 335–340

Saito, S., T. Komoda: Experimental resolution limit in the secondary electron mode for a field emission source SEM. Scanning Electron Microscopy IITRI, Chicago (1972) 129–136

Schmidt, E. H., W. Bröcker, M. Pfautsch: Kathodolumineszenz-Untersuchungen an zytologischem Material im Rasterelektronenmikroskop. (BEDO) 8 Beitr. elektronenmikroskop. Direktabb. Oberfl. (1975) 749–756

Schur, K., C. Schulte, L. Reimer: Auflösungsvermögen und Kontrast von Oberflächenstrukturen bei der Abbildung mit dem Rasterelektronenmikroskop. Z. angew. Phys. 23 (1967) 405

Schur, K., R. Blaschke, W. Uelhoff, H. Fahmer: Zum Einfluß des Betrachtungswinkels auf die Wiedergabe der Oberflächenmorphologie bei Stereoscan-Aufnahmen. (BEDO) 1 Beitr. elektronenmikroskop. Direktabb. Oberfl. (1968) 79–96

Seiler, H.: Einige aktuelle Probleme der Sekundär-

elektronemission. Z. angew. Phys. 22 (1967) 249–263

Seiler, H.: Die physikalischen Aspekte der Sekundärelektronenemission für die Elektron-Raster-Mikroskopie. Beitr. elektronenmikroskop. Direktabb. Oberfl. 1 (1968) 27–52

Seiler, H.: Determination of the „information depth" in the SEM. Scanning Electron Microscopy, IITRI, Chicago (1976) 9–16

Seiler, H., W. Wodsak: Materialdifferenzierung im Emissions-Mikroskop mit Hilfe der Energieverteilung der Elektronen. Optik 28 (1968/69) 495–504

Solomon, J. L: Non-dispersive analysis with the electron microprobe analyzer. VII. Congr. Intern. Microscopie électronique, Grenoble 1 (1970) 291

Solomon, J. L.: Use of the multichannel analyzer to make concentration maps in conjunction with the electron microprobe analyzer. VII. Congr. Intern. Microscopie électronique, Grenoble 1 (1970) 289

Swift, J. A., A. C. Brown: A technique for obtaining scanning electron micrographs in colour. J. Microsc. (Oxf.) 105 (1975) 1–14

Thompson, D. D., J. A. Esterly: Specimen discs for large-scale handing of preparations used in scanning electron microscopy. Stain. Technol. 47 (1972) 214–215

Unsworth, A., A. Hepworth: A new stereoadaptor for use with the scanning electron microscope. J. Microsc. (Oxf.) 94 (1971) 245–252

Weimann, G.: Stereotechnik mit Raster-Elektronenmikroskopen. Beitr. elektronenmikroskop. Direktabb. Oberfl. 3 (1970) 361–370

Wells, O. C.: Resolution of the topographic image in the SEM. Scanning Electron Microscopy, IITRI, Chicago (1974) 1–8

Wells, O. C.: Experimental method for measuring the electron-optical parameters of the scanning electron microscope (SEM). Scanning Electron Microscopy, IITRI, Chicago (1977) 25–32

Wells, O. C., A. N. Broers, C. G. Bremer: Method for examining solid specimens with improved resolution in the scanning electron microscope (SEM). Appl. Phys. Lett. 23 (1973) 353–355

3. Arbeiten zur Präparationstechnik

Papers on preparation techniques

Anderson, T. F.: Preparation and preservation of biological specimens – Preservation of structure in dried specimens. Proceedings Int. Conference Electron Microscopy, London 1954 122–129

Arnold, J. D., A. E. Berger, O. L. Allison: Some problemes of fixation of selected biological samples for SEM examination. Scanning Electron Microscopy, IITRI, Chicago (1971) 251–254

Bach, H., R. Blaschke, M. Bode, G. Pfefferkorn, W. Umraht: Präparationsmöglichkeiten in einer erweiterten Objektkammer am Raster-Elektronenmikroskop. Beitr. elektronenmikroskop. Direktabb. Oberfl. 4/2 (1971) 363–372

Barthlott, W., N. Ehler, R. Schill: Abtragung biologischer Oberflächen durch hochfrequenzaktivierten Sauerstoff für die Raster-Elektronenmikroskopie. Mikroskopie 32 (1976) 35–44

Bartz, G.: Ein einfaches Beschichtungsgerät für die Rasterelektronenmikroskopie. Beitr. Elektronenmikroskop. Direktabb. Oberfl. (BEDO) 7 (1974) 91–102

Böhm, E.: Zur Präparation biologischer Objektoberflächen. Beitr. elektronenmikroskop. Direktabb. Oberfl. 4/2 (1971 a) 549–554

Böhm, E.: Tieftemperaturmethoden und ihre Anwendung zur Präparation biologischer Objekte für Oberflächenuntersuchungen im REM. Beitr. elektronenmikroskop. Direktabb. Oberfl. 4/2 (1971 b) 563–574

Böhm, E.: Spezielle Entnahme-, Präparations- und Untersuchungstechniken für die Anwendung der Rasterelektronenmikroskopie in der forensischen Medizin. Beitr. gerichtl. Med. 29 (1972) 228

Boyde, A., M. H. Hobdell: Microradiography and scanning electron microscopy of bone sections. Z. Zellforsch. 94 (1969) 487

Boyde, A., C. Wood: Preparation of animal tissues for surface – scanning electron microscopy. J. Microsc. (Oxf.) 90 (1969) 221–249

Boyde, A., E. Bailey, S. J. Jones, A. Tamarin: Dimensional changes during specimen preparation for scanning electron microscopy. Scanning Electron Microscopy, IITRI, Chicago (1977) 507–518

Brüche, E.: Die Wandlung in der Oberflächenabbildung mit Elektronen. Emissions-Elektronenbild, Abdruck-Aufnahme, Raster-Elektronenbild. Phys. Bl. 25 (1969) 310–323

Carr, K. E.: Applications of scanning electron microscopy in biology. Int. Rev. Cytol. 30 (1971) 183–255

Carr, K. E., J. McGadey: Staining of biological material for the scanning electron microscope. J. Microsc. (Oxf.) 100 (1974) 323–330

Cleveland, P. H., C. W. Schneider: A simple method of preserving ocular tissue for scanning electron microscopy. Vision Res. 9 (1969) 1401–1402

Cohen, A. L.: A critical look at critical point drying theory, practice and artefacts. Scanning Electron Microscopy, IITRI, Chicago (1977) 525–536

Echlin, P., A. Burgess: Cryofracturing and low temperature scanning electron microscopy of plant material. Scanning Electron Microscopy, IITRI, Chicago (1977) 491–500

Echlin, P., A. J. Saubermann: Preparation of biological specimens for x-ray microanalysis. Scanning Electron Microscopy, IITRI, Chicago (1977) 621–638

Fecher, K.: Untersuchung dünner Schichten. Beitr. elektronenmikroskop. Direktabb. Oberfl. 4/2 (1971) 399–413

Fromme, H. G., M. Pfautsch, G. Pfefferkorn, V. Bystricky: Die Kritische Punkt-Trocknung als Präpa-

rationsmethode für die Raster-Elektronenmikroskopie. Microsc. Acta 73 (1972) 29-37

Fromme, H. G., G. Pfefferkorn, M. Pfautsch, K. Bystricky: Erfahrungen mit der Kritischen-Punkt-Trocknung als Präparationsmethode für die Rasterelektronenmikroskopie. Beitr. elektronenmikroskop. Direktabb. Oberfl. (BEDO) 5 (1972) 893-902

Fujita, T., J. Tokunaga, H. Inoue: Scanning electron microscopy of the skin using celluloid impressions. Arch. histol. J. 30 (1969) 321-326

Goldman, L., J. Vahl, R. J. Rockwell, R. Meyer, M. Franzen, P. Owens, S. Hyatt: Replica microscopy and scanning electron microscopy of laser impacts on the skin. J. invest. Derm. 52 (1969) 18-24

Grasenick, F.: Eine universelle Vorrichtung für die elektronenmikroskopische Präparation insbesonders von temperaturempfindlichen Substanzen. Proc. Europ. Reg. Conf. on Electron Microscopy Delft 1 (1960) 575

Grunbaum, B. W., S. R. Wellings: Freezedrying apparatus for preservation of ultrastructure. J. Ultrastruc. Res. 4 (1969) 117-126

Haggis, G. H.: Cryofracture of biological material. Scanning Electron Microscopy, IITRI, Chicago (1970) 97-104

de Harven, E., N. Lampen, D. Pla: Alternatives to critical point drying. Scanning Electron Microscopy, IITRI, Chicago (1977) 519-524

Hausmann, K.: Methoden zur Präparation von einzelligen Objekten für die Rasterelektronenmikroskopie. Microsc. Acta 76 (1974) 113-121

Heinzmann, U.: Verfeinerte Präparation biologischer Gewebeproben für Rasterelektronenmikroskopie. Microsc. Acta 76 (1974) 145-146

Herbst, R., A. M. Multier: Der Einfluß von Duron auf biologische Weichgewebe. Vortr. dtsch. Ges. Elektronenmikroskopie, Wien 1969

Herbst, R., A. M. Multier-Lajous, G. Kassner: A method for direct imaging of nuclei in the scanning electron microscope. Beitr. Pathol. 145 (1972) 395-400

Hiller, U., R. Blaschke: Präparationsprobleme bei tiefzerklüfteten biologischen Objekten. Beitr. elektronenmikroskop. Direktabb. Oberfl. 1 (1968) 271-274

Holm, R., G. Heyl, L. Morbitzer: Anwendung einiger Präparationsmethoden der Durchstrahlungselektronenmikroskopie für das Raster-Elektronenmikroskop. Beitr. elektronenmikroskop. Direktabb. Oberfl. 2 (1969) 153-160

Holm, R., B. Reinfandt, S. Storp: Einige Experimente mit der Leitz-Metallbeschichtungskammer. Beitr. elektronenmikroskop. Direktabb. Oberfl. (BEDO) 9 im Druck

Horridge, G. A., S. L. Tamm: Critical point drying for scanning electron microscopic study of ciliary motion. Science 163 (1969) 817-818

Howden, H. F., L. E. Ling: Scanning electron microscopy: Low-magnification pictures of uncoated zoological specimens. Science 179 (1973) 386-388

Jakopić, E.: Eine Methode zum Anätzen, schichtweisen Abbau und Verbrennen sogenannter organischer Substanzen mit aktiviertem Sauerstoff. Proc. Europ. Reg. Conf. EM Delft 1 (1960) 559

Leif, R. C., H. N. Easter, jr., R. L. Warters, R. A. Thomas, L. A. Dunlap, M. F. Austin: Centrifugal cytology. A quantitative technique for the preparation of glutaraldehydefixed cells for the light and scanning electron microscope. J. Histochem. Cytochem. 19 (1971) 203-215

de Mets, M., A. Lagasse: An investigation of some organic chemicals as cathodoluminescent dyes using the scanning electron microscope. J. Microsc. (Oxf.) 94 (1971) 1951-1956

Moor, H.: Die Gefrier-Fixation lebender Zellen und ihre Anwendung in der EM. Z. Zellforsch. 62 (1964) 546-580

Müller, H.: Präparation von technisch-physikalischen Objekten für die elektronenmikroskopische Untersuchung. Geest & Portig, Leipzig 1962

Multier, A. M., R. Herbst: Präparationsmethoden biologischer Weichgewebe für die Raster-Elektronenmikroskopie. Beitr. elektronenmikroskop. Direktabb. Oberfl. 3 (1971) 281-290

Orth, H.: Die Ionenätzung als Präparationsmethode für rasterelektronenmikroskopische Untersuchungen an Polymeren. Z. wiss. Mikr. 70 (1970) 179-188

Pameijer, C. H., R. E. Stallard: A pressureless replica technique for use with the scanning electron microscope. J. dent. Res. 51 (1972 a) 1680

Pameijer, C. H., R. E. Stallard: Application of replica techniques for use with scanning electron microscopes in dental research. J. dent. Res. 51 (1972 b) 672

Pfefferkorn, G.: Specimen preparation techniques. Scanning Electron Microscopy, IITRI, Chicago (1970) 97-104

Pfefferkorn, G., H. Gruter, M. Pfautsch: Observations on the prevention of specimen charging. Scanning Electron Microscopy, IITRI, Chicago (1972) 147-152

Pfefferkorn, G., I. H. Pawlowitzki, G. Michaeli, R. Blaschke, M. Bode: Verbesserte Abbildung von Oberflächen im Lichtmikroskop durch Anwendung von Präparationsmethoden der Raster-Elektronenmikroskopie. Beitr. elektronenmikroskop. Direktabb. Oberfl. 2 (1969) 199-206

Raith, H., P. Echlin, P. Hyde: Erste Experimente mit der Einrichtung zur Ionenätzung am Stereoscan. Beitr. elektronenmikroskop. Direktabb. Oberfl. 3 (1970) 217-226

Reimer, L.: Elektronenmikroskopische Untersuchungs- und Präparationsmethoden. Springer, Berlin 1967

Richter, I.-E.: Die Darstellung von Erythrocyten in Abhängigkeit von der Präparationsmethode. Beitr. elektronenmikroskop. Direktabb. Oberfl. 2 (1969) 213-220

Richter, I.-E.: Die direkte Abbildung enzymatisch abgebauter Gelenkoberflächen. Beitr. elektronenmikroskop. Direktabb. Oberfl. 4/2 (1971) 575-583

Schimmel, G.: Elektronenmikroskopische Methodik. Springer, Berlin 1969

Sikorski, J., W. Sprenkmann: Die Bedeutung einer neuen Behandlungstechnik von Proben aus Polymeren und Wolle unter dem Stereoscan für die Textilindustrie. Melliand Textilber. 4 (1968) 471-474

Smith, M. E., E. H. Finke: Critical point drying of soft biological material for the scanning electron microscope. Invest. Ophthal. 11 (1972) 127-132

Stuart, P. R., J. S. Osborn, S. M. Lewis: The use of

radio-frequency sputter ion etching and scanning electron microscopy to study the internal structure of biological material. Scanning Electron Microscopy, IITRI, Chicago (1969) 241–248

Tanaka, K.: Freezed resin cracking method for scanning electron microscopy of biological materials. Naturwissenschaften 59 (1972) 77

Watters, W. B., R. C. Buck: An improved simple method of specimen preparation for replicas or scanning electron microscopy. J. Microsc. (Oxf.) (1971) 185–187

Wegener, W., R. Merkle: Eine schnelle Präparationsmethode für die Untersuchung von elektrisch schlecht leitenden Substanzen im Raster-Elektronenmikroskop. Beitr. elektronenmikroskop. Direktabb. Oberfl. 1 (1968) 237–248

Witkowski, J. A., W. D. Brighton: Influence of serum on attachment of tissue to glass surfaces. Exp. Cell Res. 70 (1972) 41–48

Worthen, D. M., M. G. Wickham: Scanning electron microscopy tissue preparation. Invest. Ophthal. 11 (1972) 133–136

Zierold, K., D. Schäfer: Rasterelektronenmikroskopie und Mikrobereichsanalyse an biologischen Proben unter Verwendung einer Kühlkette. Beitr. elektronenmikroskop. Direktabb. Oberfl. (BEDO) 8 (1975) 161–174

4. Rasterelektronenmikroskopische Arbeiten zu einzelnen Objekten
Papers on scanning electron microscopic studies of individual specimens

Afrikian, E. G., G. St. Julian, L. A. Bulla: Scanning electron microscopy of bacterial colonies. Appl. Microbiol. 26 (1973) 934–937

Andrews, P. M.: Scanning electron microscopy of human and Rhesus monkey kidneys. Lab. Invest. 32 (1975) 510–518

Arakawa, M.: A scanning electron microscope study of the human glomerulus. Amer. J. Path. 64 (1971) 457–466

Arakawa, M., J. Tokunaga: Further scanning electron microscope studies of the human glomerulus. Lab. Invest. 31 (1974) 436–440

Arenberg, I. K., W. F. Marovitz, A. P. Mackenzie: Preparative techniques for the study of soft biologic tissues in the scanning electron microscope. Trans. Amer. Acad. Ophthal. Otolaryng. 75 (1971) 1332–1345

Barber, V. C., A. Boyde: Scanning electron microscopic studies of cilia. Z. Zellforsch. 84 (1968) 269–284

Barnett, W. A., M. L. Wise, E. C. Jones: Cathodoluminescence of biological molecules, macromolecules and cells. J. Microsc. (Oxf.) 105 (1975) 299–303

Barthlott, W., I. Capesius: Mikromorphologische und funktionelle Untersuchungen am Velamen radicum der Orchideen, Ber. Deutsch. Bot. Ges. 88 (1975) 379–390

Barthlott, W., N. Ehler: Raster-Elektronenmikroskopie der Epidermis-Oberflächen von Spermatophyten. Trop. Subtrop. Pflanzenwelt, Bd. 20, Akademie d. Wiss. Lit. Mainz. Steiner, Wiesbaden 1977

Baumhammers, A., J. C. Conway, D. Saltzberg, R. K. Matta: Scanning electron microscopy of supragingival calculus. J. Periodont. 44 (1973) 92–95

Beech, D. R., D. Brown: The role of the fillermatrix interface in composite restorative materials based on polymethylmethacrylate. Br. Dent. J. 133 (1972) 297–300

Beier, H. M., U. Mootz, W. Kühnel: Endokrinologische Studien an der östrogeninduzierten verzögerten Transformation und Sekretion des Kaninchenendometriums. Acta anat. (Basel) 99 (1977) 250

Bessis, M.: Living Blood Cells and Their Ultrastructure. Springer, Berlin 1973

Bill, A.: Scanning Electron microscopy of Schlemm's canal. Exp. Eye. Res. 11 (1971) 141

Böhm, E.: SEM findings on human hair following lethal high voltage injury. Elektromed. Biomed. Techn. 15 (1970) 141–155

Böhm, E.: Untersuchungen an experimentellen Stromverletzungen mit Elektronenstrahlen. Z. Rechtsmed. 67 (1970) 293–308

Böhm, E.: Some characteristic SEM findings in human skin after the action of high tension electric current. Arch. Kriminol. 147 (1971) 79–91

Böhm, E.: Untersuchungen an Kopfhaaren im Nahschußbereich mit dem Rasterelektronenmikroskop. Arch. Kriminol. 149 (1972) 65

Böhm, E.: Einige Befunde und neuere Untersuchungsmethoden zur Spezifität von Hautveränderungen nach Einwirkung von elektrischem Strom. Biomed. Techn. 17 (1972) 192, 197

Böhm, E.: Rasterelektronenmikroskopische Untersuchungen an Lungenalveolen. – Demonstration am Beispiel der Ertrinkungslunge. Beitr. gerichtl. Med. 30 (1973) 24–29

Böhm, E., H. Klingele: Einige rasterelektronenmikroskopische Befunde an menschlichen Haaren nach tödlicher Hochspannungsverletzung. Elektromedizin 15 (1970) 141–155

Böhm, E., H. Klingele: Morphologische Untersuchungen an Pulverschmauchpartikeln verschiedener Munitionsarten. Arch. Kriminol. 150 (1972) 31

Böhm, E., D. Huhn, J. Jungwirth: Raster- und transmissionselektronenmikroskopische Befunde an Erythrozytenmembranen bei Agglutination und Hämolyse. Beitr. gerichtl. Med. 31 (1973) 185

Bonilla-Musoles, F., J. Hernandez-Yago, J. V. Torres: Scanning electron microscopy of the cervix uteri. Arch. Gynäk. 216 (1974) 91–97

Booth, W. V., M. Zimmy, H. J. Kaufmann, I. Cohn: Scanning electron microscopy of small bowel strangulation obstruction. Amer. J. Surg. 125 (1973) 129–133

Boyde, A.: Correlation on ameloblast size with ena-

mel prism pattern: Use of scanning electron microscope to make surface area measurements. Z. Zellforsch. 93 (1969) 583

Boyde, A., A. N. Broers: High-resolution surface scanning electron microscopy of mineralized tissues. J. Microsc. (Oxf.) 94 (1971) 253–257

Boyde, A., M. H. Hobdell: Scanning electron microscopy of lamellar bone. Z. Zellforsch. 93 (1969) 213–231

Boyde, A., K. S. Lester: Electron microscopy of resorbing surfaces of dental hard tissues. Z. Zellforsch. 83 (1967) 538–548

Boyde, A., F. Grainger, D. W. James: Scanning electron microscopic observations of chick embryo fibroblasts in vitro, with particular reference to the movement of cells under others. Z. Zellforsch. 94 (1969) 46–55

Breipohl, W., G. J. Bijvank, H. P. Zippel: Die Oberflächenstruktur der olfaktorischen Drüsen des Goldfisches (carassius auratus). Eine rastermikroskopische Studie. Z. Zellforsch. Mikrosk. Anat. 140 (1973) 567–582

Brettle, J., A. N. Hughes: A metallurgical examination of the surgical implants which have failed in service. Injury 2 (1970) 143–154

Broers, A. N., B. J. Panessa, J. F. Gennaro: High-resolution SEM of bacteriophages 3 C and T 4. Science 189 (1975) 637–639

Brück, E., W. Stockem: Morphologische Untersuchungen an der Cuticula von Insekten. I., Die Feinstruktur der larvalen Cuticula von Blaberus trapezoideus Bur. Z. Zellforsch. Mikrosk. Anat. 132 (1972) 403–416

Brück, E., W. Stockem: Morphologische Untersuchungen an der Cuticula von Insekten. II., Die Feinstruktur der larvalen Cuticula von Periplaneta americana. Z. Zellforsch. Mikrosk. Anat. 132 (1972) 417–430

Bruni, J. E., D. G. Montemurro, R. E. Clattenburg, R. P. Singh: Scanning electron microscopy of the ependymal surface of the third ventricle after silver nitrate staining. Brain Res. 61 (1973) 207–216

Burrichter, E., F. Amelunxen, J. Vahl, T. Giele: Pollen- und Sporenuntersuchungen mit dem Oberflächen-Rasterelektronenmikroskop. Z. Pflanzenphysiol. 59 (1968) 226–237

Busch, L. C., K. Heintze: Morphologische Veränderungen der Schleimhaut isolierter Gallenblasen von Meerschweinchen nach prostaglandininduziertem Flüssigkeitstransport. Acta anat. (Basel) 99 (1977) 253

Busch, L. C., U. Mootz, W. Kühnel: Zur Oberflächenbeschaffenheit der Schleimhaut von Tube und Uterus des Kaninchens im Oestrus. Verh. anat. Ges. 71 (1977) 525–529

Cameron, H. U., I. Macnab: The structure of the meniscus of the knee joint. Clin. Orthop. 89 (1972) 215–219

Caputo, R., B. Ceccarelli: Study of normal hair and of some malformations with a scanning electron microscope. Arch. klin. exp. Derm. 234 (1969) 242–249

Carr, K. E.: Scanning electron microscope studies of human skin. Brit. J. plast. Surg. 23 (1970) 66–72

Carr, K. E., P. G. Toner: Surface studies of acute radiation injury in the mouse intestine. Virchows Arch. (Zellpathol.) 11 (1972) 201–210

Carteaud. A. J. P.: Present status of scanning electron microscopy in dermatology. Scanning Electron Microscopy, IITRI, Chicago (1970) 217–224

Carteaud, A. J. P.: Application de techniques physiques à l'étude d'échantillons biologiques en microscopie électronique par balayage. VII. Congr. Intern. Microscopie électronique, Grenoble 1 (1970 b) 473

Carter, R. H., J. D. Parkin, A. Spring: Scanning electron microscope studies of vertebrate red cells. Pathology 4 (1972) 307–310

Clarke, I. C.: Surface characteristics of human articular cartilage – A scanning electron microscope study. J. Anat. 108 (1971) 23–30

Clarke, I. C.: Articular cartilage: A review and scanning electron microscope study. J. Bone Jt Surg. 53-B (1971) 732–750

Clarke, I. C.: Correlation of SEM, replication and light microscopy studies of the bearing-surfaces in human joints. Scanning Electron Microscopy, IITRI, Chicago (1973) 659–666

Clarke, J. A., A. J. Salsbury: Surface ultramicroscopy of human blood cells. Nature (Lond.) 215 (1967) 402

Compagno, J., J. W. Grisham: Scanning electron microscopy of extrahepatic biliary obstruction. Arch. Path. 97 (1974) 348–351

Cotta, H., W. Puhl: Oberflächenbetrachtungen des Gelenkknorpels. Arch. orthop. Unfall-Chir. 68 (1970) 152–164

Dahl, E.: The innervation of the cerebral arteries in the monkey. Acta neurol. scand. 48 (1972) 431–432

Dahl, E.: The innervation of the cerebral arteries. J. Anat. 115 (1973) 53–63

Dahlgren, S. E., H. Dahlen, T. Dalhamm: Ultrastructural observations on chemically induced inflammation in guinea pig trachea. Virchows Arch. (Zellpathol.) 11 (1972) 211–213

Dey Hazra, A. K., G. Enigk, H. Konitz: Pol und Oberflächen-Ultrastruktur der Eier von Ascaris suum. Beitr. elektronenmikroskop. Direktabb. Oberfl. (BEDO) 8 (1975) 729–736

Dietrich, C. E., H. E. Franz: Untersuchungen an Grenzschicht und Vorderblatt der menschlichen Iris mittels des Raster- und Transmissions-Elektronenmikroskops. Med. Welt 24 (1973) 1659–1662

Dumitrescu, H. L., H. Hager, F. Hoffmann: Rasterelektronen-Mikroskopie der menschlichen Hornhaut. Ber. dtsch. opthalmol. Ges. 71 (1872) 656–660

Echlin, P.: The biological applications of scanning electron microscopy. VII. Congr. Intern. Microscopie électronique, Grenoble 1 (1970) 469

Ehler, N.: Mikromorphologie der Samenoberflächen der Gattung Euphorbia. Plant. Syst. Evolution 126 (1976) 189–207

Evan, A., W. G. Dail, D. Dammrose, C. Palmer: Scanning electron microscopy of tissues following removal of basement membrane and collagen. Scanning Electron Microscopy, IITRI, Chicago (1976) 203–208

Evans, J. H., I. C. Clarke: Some mechanical and structural characteristics of connective tissue. Rheol. Acta. 10 (1971) 77–82

Fadel, H. E., D. Burns, L. J. D. Zaneveld, G. D. Wilbanks, E. E. Bureschke: The surface epithelium of the human uterotubal junction. A scanning elec-

148

tron microscope study. Scanning Electron Microscopy, IITRI, Chicago (1976) 367–372

Finlay, B., I. Brown, H. Stark: Mechanical and scanning electron-microscopy studies of behaviour of the human dermis under stress. J. Anat. 105 (1969) 211

Finlay, J. B., J. A. Hunter: Visualization of collagen cross-banding in the scanning electron microscope. J. Microsc. (Oxf.) 93 (1971) 241–244

Fritsch, H., B. Urbaschek: Rasterelektronenmikroskopische Untersuchungen zur Frage der Endotoxinwirkung an der terminalen Strombahn. Zbl. Bakt. I. Abt. Orig. A 221 (1972) 527–538

Frost, H., H. Hess: Untersuchungen zur Pathogenese der arteriellen Verschlußkrankheiten. II. Beobachtungen mit dem Raster-Elektronenmikroskop über die Reparation von Endotheldefekten an Arterien. Klin. Wschr. 47 (1969) 245–249

Frost, H., H. Hess, I.-E. Richter: Untersuchungen zur Pathogenese der arteriellen Verschlußkrankheiten; eine neue Methode zum Studium früher Veränderungen auf der Gefäßwand. Klin. Wschr. 46 (1968) 1099–1109

Fujita, T., H. Inoue, T. Kodama: Scanning electron microscopy of the normal and rheumatoid synovial membranes. Arch. histol. jap. 29 (1968) 611

Gardner, D. L.: The influence of microscopic technology on knowledge of cartilage surface structure. Ann. rheum. Dis. 31 (1972) 235–258

Gardner, D. L., D. C. McGillivray: Living articular cartilage is not smooth. Ann. rheum. Dis. 30 (1971) 3

Gardner, D. L., D. H. Woodward: Scanning electron microscopy of articular surfaces. Lancet 1968 II, 1246

Gardner, D. L., D. H. Woodward: Scanning electron microscopy and replica studies of articular surfaces of guinea-pig synovial joints. Ann. rheum. Dis., 28 (1969) 379

George, R. P., R. M. Albrecht, K. B. Raper, I. B. Sachs, A. P. Mackenzie: Scanning electron microscopy of spore germination in dictyostelium discoideum. J. Bact. 112 (1972) 1383–1386

Gray, E. G., R. A. Nillis: Problems of electron stereoscopy of biological tissue. J. Cell. Sci. 3 (1968) 309–326

Greer, M. H. R. T. Greer: Progressive surface morphological changes of muscle fibers. Scanning Electron Microscopy, IITRI, Chicago (1969) 117 bis 183

Groniowski, J., M. Walski, W. Biczysko: Application of scanning electron microscopy for studies of the lung parenchyma. J. Ultrastruct. Res. 38 (1972) 473–481

Hafez, E. S., H. Kanagawa: Scanning electron microscopy of cervix uteri of cattle. Amer. J. vet. Res. 33 (1972) 2469–2474

Hafez, E. S. E.: Scanning Electron Microscopic. Atlas of Mammalian Reproduction. Thieme, Stuttgart (1975)

Hager, H., F. Hoffmann, L. Dumitrescu: Scanning electron microscopy in ophthalmology. Ann. Ophthal. 7 (1975) 1361–1371

Handschin, G.: Untersuchung von Nematoden mit dem Raster-Elektronenmikroskop. Rev. suisse Zool. 78 (1971) 574–578

Hansson, H. A.: Scanning electron microscopy of the lens of the adult rat. Z. Zellforsch. 107 (1970) 187–198

Hansson, H. A., T. Jerndal: Scanning electron microscopic studies on the development of the iridocorneal angle in human eyes. Invest. Ophthal. 10 (1971) 252–265

Hantsche, H., V. Schneider: Über Untersuchungen an Strommarken mit REM und Mikrosonde. Beitr. gerichtl. Med. 31 (1973) 192–202

Hantsche, H., W. Schwarz: Das Rasterelektronenmikroskop als Hilfsmittel zur Identifizierung von Werkzeugspuren. Arch. kriminol. 148 (1971) 24

Harris, W. A.: The maxillae of drosophila melanogaster as revealed by scanning electron microscopy. J. Morph. 138 (1972) 451–456

Hearle, J. W. S., J. T. Sparrow, P. M. Cross: The use of the scanning electron microscope. Pergamon Press, Oxford 1972

Herbst, R., A.-M. Lajons, Y. Inatsugi: Die Anwendung des JEOL-Raster-Elektronenmikroskopes für biologische Objekte. Räumliche Darstellung der menschlichen Chorionzotten. Beitr. elektronenmikroskop. Direktabb. Oberfl. 1 (1968) 297–309

Hesse, I., W. Hesse, E. Knickrehm: Die Gelenkknorpeltransplantation im Transmissions- und Rasterelektronenmikroskop. Beitr. elektronenmikroskop. Direktabb. Oberfl. (BEDO) 8 (1975) 675–682

Hesse, W., I. Hesse, E. Knickrehm: Gegenüberstellung traumatischer und nicht traumatischer Knorpelschäden. Beitr. elektronenmikroskop. Direktabb. Oberfl. (BEDO) 8 (1975) 683–690

Hessert, G. R.: Oberflächenuntersuchungen an der McKee-Farrar-Hüftendoprothese. Arch. orthop. Unfall-Chir. 70 (1971) 1–13

Heywood, V. H.: Scanning electron microscopy in the study of plant materials. Micron 1 (1969) 1–14

Hinton, H. E.: Some structure of insects as seen with the scanning electron microscope. Micron 1 (1969) 84–108

Holm, R.: Techniques for investigation of high polymers with the SEM. Scanning Electron Microscopy, IITRI, Chicago (1975) 433–440

Holm, R., G. Kämpf, W. Papenroth: Abbildung von Oberflächen mit dem Rasterelektronenmikroskop unter besonderer Berücksichtigung der Abbauvorgänge bei der Bewitterung TiO$_2$ pigmentierter Anstrichfilme. fette – seifen – anstrichmittel 75 (1973) 373–383

Horn, V., Z. Bozděch, D. Horký: Die rasterelektronenmikroskopische Untersuchung der Gelenkhohlraumzellen. Z. Orthop. 110 (1972) 331–336

Hornstra, G., S. Y. Gielen: Measurement of platelet aggregation and thrombus formation in circulating blood. Adv. exp. med. biol. 34 (1972) 321–333

Hundeiker, M.: Zur Darstellung der Gefäßarchitektur der Haut. Arch. Derm. Forsch. 245 (1972) 163–169

Hundeiker, M.: Vasculäre Regulationseinrichtungen am Hoden. Arch. Derm. Forsch. 245 (1972) 229 bis 244

Hundeiker, M., K. Brehm: Hautrelief und Capillararchitektur. Arch. Derm. Forsch. 242 (1971) 78–86

Huth, F., A. Soren, K. A. Rosenbauer, W. Klein: Fine-structural changes of the synovial membrane in arthrosis deformans. Virchows Arch. path. Anat. 359 (1973) 201–211

Irino, S., T. Ono, K. Watanabe, K. Toyota, J. Uno, N. Tagasugi, T. Murakani: SEM-studies on microvas-

cular architecture, sinus wall, and transmural passage of blood cells in the bone marrow by a new method of injection replica and non coated specimens. Scanning Electron Microscopy, IITRI, Chicago (1975) 267–274

Jain, N. C., C. S. Kond: Scanning electron microscopy of erythrocytes of dog, cat, cow, horse, sheep and goat. Res. vet. Sci. 13 (1972) 489–491

Jansson, E., M. Hannuksela, H. Eklund, H. Halme, S. Tuuri: Isolation of a mycoplasma from sarcoid tissue. J. clin. Path. 25 (1972) 837–842

Jones, S. J.: A special relationship between spherical and filamentous microorganisms in mature human dental. plaque. Arch. oral Biol. 17 (1972) 613–616

Judd, G., J. Sabo, W. Hamilton, S. Ferriss, R. Horn: SEM Microstriation characterization of bullets and contaminant particle identification. J. forens. Sci. 19 (1974) 798–811

Klein, W., K. A. Rosenbauer, L. Rupprecht, J. Krämer, J. Huth: Beitrag zur Kenntnis der juvenilen monarticulären rheumatoiden Arthritis. Virchows Arch. path. Anat. 357 (1972) 359–368

Kühnel, W., H. M. Beier, L. C. Busch, U. Mootz, G. Scheele: Oberflächenveränderungen am Kaninchenendometrium zwischen Östrus und Implantation. Acta anat. Basel 99 (1977) 286

Kurtzman, C. P., M. J. Smiley, F. L. Baker: Scanning electron microscopy of ascospores of schwanniomyces. J. Bact. 112 (1972) 1380–1382

Kuwabara, T.: Surface structure of the eye tissue. Scanning Electron Microscopy, IITRI, Chicago 1969 185–192

Kawabata, I., H. Ishii: Fiber arrangement in the tympanic membrane. Scanning electron microscope observations. Acta Otolaryng. (Stockh.) 72 (1971) 243–254

Kosaka, N., T. Tanaka, T. Takiguchi, Y. Dzeki, S. Takahara: Observation on the organ of corti with a scanning electron microscope. Acta Otolaryng. (Stockh.) 72 (1971) 377–384

Lautenbach, E.: Studien über die feinere Struktur des menschlichen Unterkieferknochens. ZWR 81 (1972) 427–437

Lenz, H.: Der Abschilferungsvorgang am Plattenepithel der Nasenschleimhaut des Menschen, eine rasterelektronenmikroskopische Studie. Arch. klin. exp. Ohr.-, Nas.- u. Kehlk.-Heilkd. 203 (1972) 30–40

Lenz, H.: Die Oberfläche von Nasenpolypen im Rasterelektronenmikroskop. Z. Laryng. Rhinol. 54 (1975) 317

Lenz, H.: Die Oberfläche der Nasenschleimhaut. Arch. klin. exp. Ohr.-, Nas.- u. Kehlk.-Heilkd. 202 (1972) 353–359

Lenz, H.: Rasterelektronenmikroskopische Darstellung freier Zellen, Bakterien und Fremdpartikel der Tonsillenoberfläche. H.N.O. 20 (1972) 78–81

Lenz, H.: Die Oberfläche der Nasenschleimhaut bei Rhinitis vasomotorica im Rasterelektronenmikroskop. Arch. klin. exp. Ohr.-, Nas.- u. Kehlk.-Heilk. 202 (1972) 353–359

Lenz, H.: Rasterelektronenmikroskopische Untersuchungen an der menschlichen Tonsille, Arch. klin. exp. Ohren-, Nas.- u. Kehlk.-Heilk. 199 (1971) 599–604

Lenz, H.: Räumliche Betrachtungen der Tonsillen-

nenstruktur mit Hilfe des Rasterelektronenmikroskops. Z. Laryng. Rhinol. 51 (1972) 262–274

Lenz, H.: Three-dimensional surface representation of the ciliafree nasal mucosa of man. A scanning-electron-microscopical study. Acta otolaryng. (Stockh.) 76 (1973) 47–57

Lenz, P., I. E. Richter, H. Huber: Oberflächenuntersuchungen von zahnärztlichen Kunststoffen mittels des Raster-Sekundärelektronenmikroskops Stereoscan. Dtsch. zahnärztl. Z. 23 (1968) 717–723

Lewis, S. M., P. R. Stuart: Ultrastructure of the red blood cell. Proc. roy. Soc. Med. 63 (1970) 465

Lim, D. J.: A scanning electron microscopic investigation on otosclerotic stapes. Ann. Otol. (St. Louis) 79 (1970) 780–799

Lim, D. J.: Morphological and physiological correlates in cochlear and vestibular sensory epithelia. Scanning Electron Microscopy, IITRI, Chicago (1976) 269–274

Lindeman, H. H., G. Bredberg: Scanning electron microscopy of the organ of corti after intense auditory stimulation: Effects on stereocilia and cuticular surface of hair cells. Arch. klin. exp. Ohr.-, Nas.- u. Kehlk.-Heilkd. 203 (1972) 1–15

Lindenfelser, R., W. Krönert, H. Orth: Strukturen der Knochenspongiosa. Virchows Arch. path. Anat. 5 (1970) 201–208.

Lindenfelser, R., J. Schoemackers, P. Haubert, W. Krönert: Der spongiöse Knochen beim primären Hyperparathyreoidismus. Strukturanalyse mit dem Raster-Elektronenmikroskop. Virchows Arch. path. Anat. 9 (1971) 333–342

Lindenfelser, R., H. P. Schmitt, P. Haubert: Vergleichende rasterelektronenmikroskopische Knochenuntersuchungen bei primärem und sekundärem Hyperparathyreoidismus zur Frage der periosteocytären Osteolyse. Virchows Arch. path. Anat. 360 (1973) 141–154

Longster, G. H., L. A. Tovey: The effects of certain blood-grouping sera on the red-cell surface as seen by the scanning electron microscope. Brit. J. Haemat. 23 (1972) 635–640

Ludwig, H., H. Metzger: The re-epithelization of the endometrium after menstrual desquamation. Scanning Electron Microscopy, IITRI, Chicago (1976) 351–368

Ludwig, H., H. Metzger: The Human Female Reproductive Tract – A Scanning Electron Microscopic Atlas. Springer, Berlin (1976)

Ludwig, H., H. Junkermann, H. Klingele: Oberflächenstrukturen der menschlichen Placenta im Rasterelektronenmikroskop. Arch. Gynäk. 210 (1971) 1–20

Ludwig, G., H. Wolf, H. Metzger: Zur Ultrastruktur der Tubeninnenflächen im Rasterelektronenmikroskop. Arch. Gynäk. 212 (1972) 380–396

Lundsteen, C., J. Philip: Microphotometry of banded human chromosomes. High resolving power by direct scanning of the specimen compared with scanning on microphotographs. J. oral. Surg. 11 (1974) 196–200

Lung, B., G. F. Bahr: Scanning electron microscopy of critical point dried human spermatozoa. J. Reprod. Fertil. 31 (1972) 317–318

Lupulescu, A., C. B. Boyd: Lung cancer: A transmis-

sion and scanning electron microscopic study. Cancer (Philad.) 29 (1972) 2530–2548

McCall, J. G.: Scanning electron microscopy of articular surfaces. Lancet 30 (1968) 1194

Maclean, H., W. M. Haining: Scanning electron microscopy of cornea. Trans. ophthal. Soc. U. K. 91 (1971) 31–40

Mahrle, G., C. Orfanos: Haar und Haaroberfläche. Variationen des Aufbaus und des Cuticulamusters verschiedener Haare und verschiedener Haarabschnitte. Hautarzt 22 (1971) 113–120

Mahrle, G., C. E. Orfanos: Stereo-elektronenmikroskopische Untersuchungen an der Venenwand. Das normale Venenendothel. Arch. Derm. Forsch. 242 (1971) 43–54

Mahrle, G., C. E. Orfanos: Das Endothel gesunder und varicöser Venen-Untersuchungen mit dem Stereo-Elektronenmikroskop. Hautarzt 22 (1971) 486–489

Mahrle, G., C. E. Orfanos: Endothelveränderungen bei Varicosis. Stereo-Elektronenmikroskopische Befunde. Arch. Derm. Forsch. 242 (1972) 216–228

Mahrle, G., R. Christenhuß, C. Orfanos: Haar und Haarcuticula im Raster-Elektronenmikroskop. Arch. klin. exp. Derm. 235 (1969) 295–300

Marini, D.: Scanning electron microscopy of the gastric mucosa of rats after a stressful treatment. VII. Congr. Intern. Microscopie électronique, Grenoble 3 (1970) 887–888

Mason, R. G., R. W. Shermer, N. F. Rodman: Reactions of blood with nonbiologic surfaces. Ultrastructural and clotting studies with normal and coagulation factors deficient bloods. Amer. J. Path. 69 (1972) 271–288

Meschede, F., H. Vogel: Orientierende rasterelektronenmikroskopische Untersuchungen über den Kunststoff Palakav. Z. Orthop. 112 (1974) 419–426

Meylan, B. A., B. G. Butterfield: Three-Dimensional Structure of Wood. Chapman & Hall, London 1972

Mitosinka, G. T., J. I. Thornton, T. L. Hayes: The examination of cystolithic hairs of cannabis and other plants by means of the scanning electron microscope. J. forens. Sci. Soc. 12 (1972) 521–529

Möllmann, H., B. von Klot-Heydenfeldt, D. H. Niemeyer, H. Alfes: Vergleichende Untersuchungen der Korngrößenverteilung und Partikelbeschaffenheit einiger Corticoid-Kristallsuspensionen. Int. J. clin. Pharmacol. 5 (1972) 434–443

Möllmann, H., C. Bigalke, A. Groß, H. Wagner: Klinisch-pharmakologische Aspekte unterschiedlicher Betamethason-Kristallsuspensionen. Fortschr. Med. 14 (1977) 972–978

Möllmann, H., E. Danners, C. Bigalke, J. Kindler: Klinische Untersuchungen zur Verweildauer intraartikulär applizierter Kortikoidkristallsuspensionen. Therapiewoche 24 (1974) 4796

Morgenroth, K., A. Verhagen: Die Oberflächenstruktur der Portioektopie im Rasterelektronenmikroskop. Arch. Gynäk. 212 (1972) 423–429

Münzenberg, K. J., G. Flajs, J. Roggatz, F. Süßenbach: Korrosionsbedingte Oberflächenschäden am lebenden Gewebe, insbesondere am Knochen, im rasterelektronenmikroskopischen Bild. Z. Orthop. 110 (1972) 336–341

Münzenberg, K. J., G. Flajs, J. Roggatz: Rasterelektronenmikroskopische Untersuchungen krankhaf-

ter Knochenstrukturen, insbesondere bei Ostitis deformans Paget. Z. Orthop. 109 (1971) 760–768

Nawa, T., A. Terauchi, T. Nagata: Observation of cultivated cells by scanning electron microscopy and differential interference microscopy. Arch. histol. Jap. 34 (1972) 491–500.

Netzel, H.: Die Bildung der Gehäusewand bei der Thekamöbe Centropyxis discoides (Rhizopoda, Testacea). Z. Zellforsch. Mikr. Anat. 135 (1972) 45–54

Netzel, H.: Die Schalenbildung bei Difflugia oviformis (Rhizopoda, Testacea). Z. Zellforsch. Mikr. Anat. 135 (1972) 55–61

Netzel, H.: Morphogenese des Gehäuses von Euglypha rotunda (Rhizopoda, Testacea). Z. Zellforsch. Mikr. Anat. 135 (1972) 63–69

Nemanic, M. K., D. R. Bitelka: A scanning electron microscopy study of the lactating mammary gland. J. Cell. Biol. 48 (1971) 410–415

Newesely, H.: Entwicklungen der Implantationstechnik in der Zahnheilkunde. Österr. Z. Stomat. 74 (1977) 302–314

Noack, W., L. Dumitrescu, J. U. Schweichel: Scanning and electron microscopical investigations of the surface structures of the lateral ventricles in the cat. Brain Res. 46 (1972) 121–129

Nolte, A., H. G. Fromme, F. Johannaber: Die Darstellung einiger Spermien im Raster-Elektronenmikroskop. Beitr. elektronenmikroskop. Direktabb. Oberfl. 3 (1970) 291–298

Ohnsorge, J.: Elektronenoptische Untersuchungen von Metallimplantaten mit dem Rasterelektronenmikroskop. Habilitationsarbeit, Universitätskliniken Köln 1970

Ohnsorge, J.: Untersuchungen von Knochenzement mit dem Rasterelektronenmikroskop. Vortr. dtsch. Ges. Orthop. Traum. Kiel 1970. Enke, Stuttgart 1971 a (S. 379–381)

Ohnsorge, J.: Oberflächenanalysen von Metallimplantaten mit dem Rasterelektronenmikroskop. Vortr. dtsch. Ges. Orthop. Traum., Kiel 1970. Enke, Stuttgart 1971 b (S. 267–269)

Ohnsorge, J.: Investigation of metal implants by scanning electron microscopy. Acta orthop. belg. 37 (1971 c) 632–635

Ohnsorge, J., R. Holm: Die Spongiosafeinstruktur des Hüftkopfes im rasterelektronenmikroskopischen Bild. Arch. orthop. Unfall-Chir. 68 (1970 a) 15–27

Ohnsorge, J., R. Holm: Änderungen der Spongiosafeinstruktur unter dem Einfluß des auspolymerisierenden Knochenzementes. Untersuchungen mit dem Rasterelektronenmikroskop. Z. Orthop. 107 (1970 b) 405–411

Ohnsorge, J., R. Holm: Zellen des Portio-Abstrichs im Raster-Elektronenmikroskop. Münch. med. Wschr. 112 (1970 c) 844–845

Ohnsorge, J., R. Holm: Rasterelektronenmikroskopische Untersuchungen an Metallimplantaten nach Osteosynthese. Sonderbände der Praktischen Metallographie 6 (1976) 118–125

Ohnsorge, J., G. Schütt, R. Holm: Rasterelektronenmikroskopische Untersuchungen des gesunden und arthrotischen Gelenkknorpels. Z. Orthop. 108 (1970) 268–277

Ohnsorge, J., W. Steinbeck: Rasterelektronenmikroskopische Darstellung von Korrosionseffekten an

scheinbar unbeschädigten Metallimplantaten. Vortrag deutsch. Ges. Orthop. Traum. Wien 1969, Enke, Stuttgart 1970 (S. 302-304)

Orfanos, C., R. Christenhuß, G. Mahrle: Die normale und psoriatische Hautoberfläche. Vergleichende Beobachtungen mit dem Raster-Elektronenmikroskop. Arch. klin. exp. Derm. 235 (1969) 284-294

Orfanos, C., G. Mahrle, R. Christenhuß: Verhornungsstörungen am Haar bei Psoriasis. Eine Studie im Raster-Elektronenmikroskop. Arch. klin. exp. Derm. 236 (1970 a) 107-114

Orfanos, C., G. Mahrle, M. Piroth: Haarschäden durch Trichophyton Schönleinii im Raster-Elektronenmikroskop vor und nach antimykotischer Behandlung. Klin. Wschr. 48 (1970 b) 1111-1119

Orfanos, C. E., G. Schaumburg-Lever, W. F. Lever: Alterations of Cell Surfaces as a Pathogenetic Factor in Psoriasis. Arch. Derm. 107 (1973) 38-46

Orita, K., I. Yamamoto, T. Murakami: Scanning electron microscopy of contactual interaction of sensitized lymphocytes with homologous target cells. Acta Med. Okayama 25 (1971) 525-536

Pawlowitzki, I. H., R. Blaschke: Probleme der Chromosomendarstellung im Rasterelektronenmikroskop. Beitr. elektronenmikroskop. Direktabb. Oberfl. 1 (1968) 249-260

Pawlowitzki, I. H., R. Blaschke, R. Christenhuß: Darstellung von Chromosomen im Raster-Elektronenmikroskop nach Enzymbehandlung. Naturwissenschaften 55 (1968) 63-64

Pfautsch, M., H. G. Fromme, G. Forck: Rasterelektronenmikroskopische Beobachtungen an der gesunden menschlichen Haut. Beitr. elektronenmikroskop. Direktabb. Oberfl. 3 (1970) 319-326

Piekarski, K.: Fracture of bone. J. appl. Phys. 41 (1970) 215

Pier, A. C., K. R. Rhoades, T. L. Hayes, J. Gallagher: Scanning electron microscopy of selected dermatophytes of veterinary importance. Amer. J. vet. Res. 33 (1972) 607-613

Polliack, A.: Surface features of circulating human leukemic cells: Experience with 175 cases of leukemia examined by scanning electron microscopy. Scanning Electron Microscopy, IITRI, Chicago (1976) 31-38

Puhl, W.: Rasterelektronenmikroskopische Untersuchungen zur Frage früher Knorpelschädigungen durch leukocytäre Enzyme. Arch. orthop. Unfall-Chir. 70 (1971) 87-97

Puhl, W.: Mikromorphologie gesunder Gelenkknorpeloberflächen. Z. Orthop. 112 (1974) 262-272

Puhl, W., V. Iyer: SEM observations on the structure of the articular cartilage surface in normal and pathological conditions. Scanning Electron Microscopy, IITRI, Chicago (1973) 675-682

Puhl, W., H. O. Dustmann, K.-P. Schulitz, Knorpelveränderungen bei experimentellem Hämarthros. Z. Orthop. 109 (1971) 475-486

Puhl, W., K.-P. Schulitz: Morphologische Untersuchungen über die Polymerisation von Knochenzement. Arch. orthop. Unfall-Chir. 69 (1971) 300

Rauh, W., W. Barthlott, N. Ehler: Morphologie und Funktion der Testa staubförmiger Flugsamen. Bot. Jahrb. Systematik 96 (1975) 353-374

Redler, J., L. Marilyn, Ph. D. Zimmy: Scanning electron microscopy of normal and abnormal articular cartilage and synovium. J. Bone Jt Surg. 52 A (1970) 1395-1404

Refior, H. J.: Altersabhängige Veränderungen der Meniscusoberfläche - Untersuchungen mit dem Rasterelektronenmikroskop. Arch. orthop. Unfall-Chir. 71 (1971) 316-323

Resch, A., R. Blaschke: Die Anwendung des Raster-Elektronenmikroskops in der Holzanatomie. Planta (Berl.) 78 (1968) 85-88

Reumuth, H.: Coccolithen. Mikrokosmos Stuttgart 57 (1968) 1-6

Richter, I.-E.: Gestalt und Oberfläche von Zellen im Raster-Elektronenmikroskop. Z. wiss. Mikr. 70 (1970 a) 39-48

Richter, I.-E.: Rasterelektronenmikroskopische Untersuchungen von Zelloberflächen. Zool. Anz. Suppl. 33 (1970 c) 631-635

Richter, I.-E.: Raster-Elektronenmikroskopie bei der Untersuchung von Knochenfeinstrukturen. Mat. Med. Nordm. 23 (1971) 226-233

Richter, I.-E., J. Altwein, U. B. Mairose: Rasterelektronenoptische Untersuchungen osmotisch bedingter Erythrozytenveränderungen. Ärztl. Lab. 17 (1971) 259-265

Richter, I.-E., K. Vogel, H.-J. Huber: Die Untersuchung unfixierter pflanzlicher Objekte mit dem Raster-Elektronenmikroskop Stereoscan. Z. wiss. Mikr. 69 (1968) 94-103

Riede, U. N., W. Villiger, J. Torhorst: Oberflächenfeinstruktur der Neointima menschlicher Arterien nach Endarteriektomie. Virchows Arch. path. Anat. 10 (1972) 83-87

Riedel, H., J. Vahl, G. Winkelmann: Untersuchungen über die Mikromorphologie getragener Palakav-Füllungen mit Hilfe des Raster-Elektronenmikroskops. Dtsch. zahnärztl. Z. 26 (1971) 267-273

Rohrschneider, I., I. Wetstein: Vergleichende rasterelektronenmikroskopische Untersuchungen an der Froschlunge nach Lufttrocknung und nach Anwendung der „Critical-Point"-Methode. Mikroskopie 29 (1973) 116-121

Sasa, M., A. Shirasaka, Y. Wada, H. Suzuki, H. Tanaka, S. Noda: The use of scanning electron microscopy in morphology and taxonomy of some mites and mosquitoes. Jap. J. exp. Med. 41 (1971) 135-158

Saxton, C. A.: Scanning electron microscope study of plaque formation. Caries Res. 6 (1972) 75

Schäfer, D., M. Seiffert, J. Höper: Zur Darstellung des Gefäßnetzes in der Rattenleber mit Hilfe der Rasterelektronenmikroskopie. Mikroskopie (im Druck)

Schäfer, D., E. Seidl, H. Acker, H.-P. Keller, D. W. Lübbers: Arteriovenous anastomoses in the cat carotid body. Z. Zellforsch. 142 (1973) 515-524

Scheid, W., H. Traut: Visualization by scanning electron microscopy of achromatic lesions (gaps) induced by X-rays in chromosomes of vicia faba. Mutation Res. 11 (1971) 253-255

Schneider, V.: Über die Untersuchung von Haaren mit dem Rasterelektronenmikroskop. Z. Rechtsmed. 71 (1972) 94-103

Schneider, V.: REM-Untersuchung zur Ertrinkungslunge. Beitr. gerichtl. Med. 29 (1972) 266

Schneider, V.: REM-Untersuchung zur Alterung von Samenfäden. Beitr. gerichtl. Med. 30 (1973) 394

152

Schneider, V.: Über REM-Untersuchungen an vital und postmortal entstandenen Thromben. Z. Rechtsmed. 74 (1974) 47

Schwinn, F. J.: Die Darstellung von Pilzsporen im Raster-Elektronenmikroskop. Phytopath. 64 (1969) 376–379

Schulz, H. P., R. Holm: Stereoskopische Aufnahmen metazoischer Parasiten mit dem Rasterelektronenmikroskop. Jahresberichte des naturwissenschaftlichen Vereins Wuppertal, H. 26 (1973) 84–92

Schur, K., G. Pfefferkorn: Das Photo-Emissionselektronenmikroskop (Photo-EEM) und das Raster-Elektronenmikroskop (REM) als Metallmikroskope – ein Vergleich. Radex-Rundschau 3 (1970) 227–234

Schulte-Wrede, S., R. Wetzstein: Raster-Elektronenmikroskopie von Spermien des Hausschafs (ovis ammon aries, L.) Z. Zellforsch. Mikr. Anat. 134 (1972) 105–127

Schweiger, H. G., S. Berger, K. Kloppstech, K. Apel, M. Schweiger: Some fine structural and biochemical features of Acetabularia major (Chlorophyta, Dasycladaceae) grown in the laboratory. Phycologia 13 (1974) 11–20

Sclippa, E., K. Piekarski: Carbon fiber reinforced polyethylene für possible orthopedic uses. J. biomed. Mater Res. 7 (1973) 59–70

Seed, T. M., J. P. Kreier, S. N. Al-Abassy, R. M. Pfister: Trypanosoma cruzi: The ultrastructure of culture forms as examined by carbon replication, freeze-etching and scanning electron microscopy. Z. Tropenmed. Parasit. 24 (1973) 146–160

Semlitsch, M.: Oberflächenuntersuchungen an Metallen und Kunststoffen für künstliche Hüftgelenke mit dem Raster-Elektronenmikroskop. Technische Rundschau, Sulzer 1971

Shetsiruli, L. T., K. G. Apridonidze: Studies of the mycotic process caused by Trichophyton rubrum (in vitro) with transmission and scanning electron microscopy. Castellania 4 (1976) 177–182

Sheykholeslam, Z., M. G. Buonocore: Bonding of resins to phosphoric acid-etched enamel surfaces of permanent and deciduous teeth. J. dent. Res. 51 (1972) 1572–1576

Shimada, T., D. J. Lim: The fiber arrangement of the human tympanic membrane. A scanning electron microscopic observation. Ann. Otol. (St. Louis) 80 (1971) 210–217

Skoluda, D., K. Wegner, I. Richter: Rasterelektronenoptische Untersuchungen am Urothel der menschlichen Harnblase. Urologie 11 (1972) 338–340

Speeter, D., J. Ohnsorge: Rasterelektronenmikroskopisch erfaßbare Schußzeichen am Knochen. Z. Rechtsmed. 73 (1973) 137–143

Steigleder, G. K., U. Osselmann, R. Möschel, G. Mahrle: Strukturanalyse normalen und pathologischen Hodengewebes. Derm. Mschr. 158 (1972) 393–404

Stendel, W., R. Holm: Oberflächenstrukturen von Mund- und Haftwerkzeugen einiger Ektoparasiten. Vet. med. Nachr. 1/2 (1975) 188–208

Sutfin, L. V., R. E. Ogilvie: Scanning electron microscopy and energy dispersion microanalysis of metallographically polished dental amalgam surfaces. J. dent. Res. 51 (1972) 1048–1054

Tanaka, K., R. Makino, A. Ilno: The fine structure of human somatic chromosomes studied by SEM. Arch. histol. Jap. 32 (1970) 203–211

Tillmann, B., I. Pietzsch-Rohrschneider, H. L. Huenges: The Human Vocal Cord Surface. Cell Tiss. Res. 185 (1977) 279–283

Tokunaga, J., M. Edanaga, Y. Masu, T. Fujita: Isolated renal glomeruli for scanning electron microscopy. J. Electron Microsc. (Tokyo) 24 (1975) 109–114

Troughton, J., L. A. Donaldson: Probing Plant Structure. A Scanning Electron Microscope Study of some Anatomical Features in Plants and the Relationship of these Structures to Physiological Processes. Chapman & Hall, London 1972

Urbaschek, B., H. Fritsch, I.-E. Richter: Erste Beobachtungen mit dem Rasterelektronenmikroskop in der Frühphase der Endotoxinwirkung an der terminalen Strombahn. Klin. Wschr. 47 (1969) 1166–1170

Vahl, J., H. D. Mierau: Feinstrukturelle Untersuchungen am transparenten Wurzeldentin kariesfreier Zähne. Dtsch. zahnärztl. Z. 26 (1971) 365–377

Vahl, J., H. D. Mierau, H. Dechsner: Elektronenmikroskopische Untersuchungen an Zahndünnschliffen nach Ionenbeschuß bei unterschiedlichen Einfallswinkeln. Dtsch. zahnärztl. Z. 27 (1972) 909–916

Vahl, J., G. Pfefferkorn: Elektronenoptische Untersuchungen der durch Laser-Beschuß hervorgerufenen Veränderungen an Zahnhartsubstanzen. Dtsch. zahnärztl. Z. 22 (1967) 386–394

Walker, P. S., J. Sikorski, D. Dowson, M. D. Longfield, V. Wright, T. Buckley: Behaviour of synovial fluid on surfaces of articular cartilage. A scanning electron microscope study. Ann. rheum. Dis. 28 (1969) 1–14

Weise, R. W.: Ascaris suum: A scanning electron microscope study. J. Parasit. 59 (1973) 141–146

Wersaell, J.: Morphology of the vestibular receptors in mammals. Progr. Brain Res. 37 (1972) 3–17

Weindl, A., R. J. Joynt: Ultrastructure of the ventricular walls. Three-dimensional study of regional specialization. Arch. Neurol. (Chic.) 26 (1972) 420–427

Wheeler, E. E., J. B. Gavin, P. B. Herdson: A scanning electron microscopy study of human heart valve allografts. Pathology 4 (1972) 185–192

Williams, S. T., F. L. Davies: Use of a scanning electron microscope for the examination of actinomycetes. J. gen. Microbiol. 48 (1967) 171–177

Wollweber, H., R. Holm: Untersuchungen über die Sporen höherer Pilze im Raster-Elektronenmikroskop. Westfälische Pilzbriefe 8 (1971) 180–191

Wollweber, H., R. Holm: Untersuchungen über die Sporen höherer Pilze im Rasterelektronenmikroskop. Stereoskopische Aufnahmen von Sporen. Jahresberichte des naturwissenschaftlichen Vereins, Wuppertal, H. 26 (1973) 71–83

Worthen, D. M.: Scanning electron microscopic study of the interior of Schlemm's canal in the human eye. Amer. J. Ophthal. 74 (1972) 35–40

Zimmy, M. L., I. Redler: Scanning electron microscopy of chondrocytes. Acta anat. (Basel) 83 (1972) 398–402

Ziswiler, V.: Die Darstellung von Oberflächenstrukturen des Verdauungstraktes mit Hilfe des Raster-Elektronenmikroskopes. Rev. Suisse Zool. 72 (1972) 1176–1188

5. Sonstige Arbeiten aus angrenzenden Fachgebieten

Other papers from adjoining fields

Benninghoven, A.: Analysis of submonolayers on silver by negative secondary ion emission. phys. stat. sol. 34 K (1969) 169

Benninghoven, A.: Die Analyse monomolekularer Festkörperoberflächenschichten mit Hilfe der Sekundärionenemission. Z. Phys. 230 (1970) 403

Chandler, J. A.: Neue Anwendung des analytischen Elektronenmikroskops EMMA-4. Beitr. elektronenmikroskop. Direktabb. Oberfl. 4 (1971) 157–172

Gerlach, R. L., N. C. MacDonald: Recent advances in scanning auger instrumentation. Scanning Electron Microscopy, IITRI, Chicago (1976) 199–206

Hoder, D.: Holographische Stereogramme in der Rasterelektronenmikroskopie. Beitr. elektronenmikrosk. Direktabb. Oberfl. 8 (1975) 255–266

Hodges, G. M., M. D. Muir: Autoradiography of biological tissues in the scanning electron microscope. Nature (Lond.) 247 (1974) 383–385

Höhling, H. J., T. A. Hall: Elektronenstrahlmikroanalyse als quantitative histologische Methode. Naturwissenschaften 56 (1969) 622–629

Holm, R.: ESCA und SIMS: Eine Gegenüberstellung zweier Oberflächenanalysenmethoden. Metalloberfläche Angew. Elektrochemie 27 (1973) 199–207

Holm, R.: Überlegungen zur Auger-Mikroanalyse aus der Sicht des Anwenders. Beitr. elektronenmikroskop. Direktabb. Oberfl. BEDO 6 (1973) 147–161

Holm, R., J. Ohnsorge: Oxidschichtuntersuchungen an reinen Metallen mit Hilfe von ESCA. Arch. orthop. Unfall-Chir. 82 (1975) 263–270

Holm, R., J. Ohnsorge: ESCA-Untersuchungen von Metallimplantatoberflächen. Sonderbände der Praktischen Metallographie 6 (1976) 126–134

Holm, R., S. Storp: Monolagenanalyse an „schmutzigen" Oberflächen? Phys. Bl. 32 (1976) 342–352

Joy, D. C., D. M. Maher: Sensitivity limits for thin Specimen x-ray analysis. Scanning Electron Microscopy, IITRI, Chicago (1977) 325–334

Martin, F. W.: Is a scanning ion microscope feasible? Science 179 (1973) 173–175

Middleman, L. M., J. D. Geller: Trace element analysis using x-ray excitation with an energy dispersive spectrometer on a scanning electron microscope. Scanning Electron Microscopy, IITRI, Chicago (1976) 171–178

Ohnsorge, J.: Ionenoptische Untersuchungen der Passivschicht von Metallimplantaten. Z. Orthop. 110 (1972) 962–964

Robertson, A. J.: The electron probe microanalyser and its applications in medicine. Phys. in Med. biol. 13 (1968) 505–522

Siegbahn, K., C. Nordling, A. Fahlman, R. Nordberg, K. Hamrin, J. Hedman, G. Johansson, T. Bergmark, S.-E. Karlsson, J. Lindgren, B. J. Lindberg: ESCA; Atomic, Molecular and Solid State Structure Studied by Means of Electron Spectroscopy. Almquist & Wiksell, Stockholm 1967

Sachverzeichnis

Subject Index